BEYOND THE FRAY

BIGFOOT

BEYOND THE FRAY
Publishing

SHANNON LEGRO
G. MICHAEL HOPF

Printed in the United States of America

First Printing, 2019

ISBN 978-1-7344198-0-1

Beyond The Fray Publishing, a division of Beyond The Fray, LLC
San Diego, CA 92127

www.beyondthefraypublishing.com

ACKNOWLEDGMENTS

This book is just a part of my journey, a journey of discovery that has taken me years, and over these years I have met many wonderful people. To those below, I am grateful for your help, support, advice, contribution, love and encouragement. I couldn't be where I am without each and every one of you. If I do forget someone, please forgive me.

Wes Germer of Sasquatch Chronicles, thanks for trusting in me and allowing me to be a part of your show. You introduced me to the art of interviewing. It never would have occurred to me I'd be any good at it. (Opinions may vary on that last part.)

Wil Jevning, thank you for always being patient, you were clearly far more adept at speaking to witnesses than I, and thank you for always sharing your knowledge on the subject of Sasquatch.

Fellow Las Vegan George Knapp, you are

the ultimate example of what a radio host and investigative journalist is.

Clyde Lewis and Howard Hughes for putting out fantastic content that I can't get enough of. I've learned a lot from you both.

Sam Shearon for helping create *iNTO THE FRAY*. Without your creative mind, skills, and selflessness, it absolutely wouldn't be what it is today.

Ryan Sprague for devoting so much of your valuable time to be a massive part of this show. Proud to call you a friend.

Brennon Storr for being an editor-in-chief to my horribly unorganized thoughts.

Dave Schrader for believing in me enough to vote for me to be a guest host on one of the most ultimate shows, *Midnight in the Desert*, a legacy of the incredible Art Bell.

Seth and Adrienne Breedlove. Two wonderful people making fantastic monster movies, and choosing to include me in them. Hugs to Bubby.

The CryptoFam: Eric and Kerrie

Fargiorgio, Sean Forker, and James Baker.

Brett Anthony for creating a beautiful website.

Tanek for allowing me to utilize your track 'Seasons' as my opener...and Electus for my closing.

The great Alan Watts, whose spoken word adds power to an already powerful track.

G. Michael Hopf for believing in my content enough to say, "I have an idea..."

Investigators and authors, Linda Godfrey, Lyle Blackburn, Phil Poling, and Jesus Jr. (to name a few) for coming on with me way back when I was a greenhorn during 'Show Notes with Shannon.'

The Olympic Project: David Ellis, Shane Corson, and Derek Hayes.

Donna D. and Ramona Bell. Two lovely ladies whom I don't talk to enough, but I know they're there for me.

Kipp Morrill. A true baller, blaze-battlin' mofo, and all around great guy. Always a positive force, keeping it light in the crazy world of Bigfoot.

My daughter and DD, for their patience during the never-ending cycle of interviews.

My stepbrother, Shawn Kevin Jason—we meet again!

David Paulides for always granting me an interview, even when it was at an ungodly hour.

My sea creature guru, Max Hawthorne. He wrestles with and conquers words and gators. Really though.

My resident demonologist, Jon-Paul Capece. Because...demons, baby!

Some of my favorite and most-oft visited guests...Steve Stockton, Sysco Murdoch, Mark and Kari Muncy, and John Olsen.

My buddy Andy Matzke.

Brett Manning for her beautiful artwork and kind words since the beginning.

A legit crew of amazing friends: Brandon Dalo, Zac Palmisano, Jason Utes, Adam Duggan, Mark Matzke.

My Insiders, who think I'm worthy

enough to spend some of their hard-earned money on extra content from me.

My "Weird Writers" who have contributed to the blog over the years

Also, Micah Hanks, Caleb Hanks, Jeremy London, the late JC Johnson, Derek Hayes, Cameron Hale, Kyle Philson, Joe Decker, Chris Bsales, Vance Nesbitt, Jennifer Ann, Cory Lekopy, the entire Pinsonnaults crew, Darryl Jackson, Jimmy Moore, Paul Bestall, Brian Burgess, Wil Johnson, Cindy Crews, Jeffrey Kelley, Scott Santa, John Mijares, Patrick Harnett, Bruce Kelley, The Kirkland's, Gord Olliver, Greg Ludwig, Ryan Skinner, Italia Gandolfo, Father Jack Ashcraft, Ty Wilson, Rob and Vickie Graves, Joe LeBlanc, Brian Sanders, Jean St. Jean, Jeff Beyers, Charlie Shafter, Christopher Garetano, David Floyd, Efrum Ferguson, Jeff Williams, Josh Carnell, Carl Platz, No Shoes Curly, Pedro Morales, Dave Hallet, Bobby Reich, Bono Russell, David Weatherly, Joe DH, Johnny Calderon, Rob Kristoffersen, Ray Gardner, Michael Del

Russi, Brad Lockwood, Jim Perry, Brandon T in Cali, John J in FL, Luke Phillips, Sean Wick, Pamela H, Lon Strickler, Jeremy Enfinger, Daniel Antal, Jason Pentrail, Ken Gerhard, Jen Devillier, Mary Elizabeth Suprenant, Dustin Rayz, the Morelands, Kirk Brandenburg, the Browns, Ashe Kapoor, Craig Woolheater, Bob Gimlin, Abe Del Rio, Angie Purpura, Tracy Savage, Tim Weisberg, Michelle Freed-Bulgatz, Keith Rowland, Race and Robin Hobbs, Bill Forte, Paul Bestall, Mattie Victoria, Gloom 82, Amy Bue, Chris Holm, the Frick's, and Thrst.

And lastly and most importantly...a huge thanks to all those willing to share their stories, and to the ones listening.

- Shannon

PRAISE FOR BEYOND THE FRAY

"An often terrifying, occasionally nerve-wracking, frequently thought-provoking jaunt through back woods, haunted by what you might have thought was simply a myth."

- Seth Breedlove, filmmaker

"Shannon LeGro's new book is almost unique, in the sense that it is 100 percent focused on incredible eyewitness testimony. Shannon gets right to the heart of what it means to see a Bigfoot!"

- Nick Redfern, author of *The Bigfoot Book.*

"An amazing collection of chilling, first-person accounts that will make you think twice about going into the woods."

- Lyle Blackburn, author of *The Beast of Boggy Creek.*

"Shannon LeGro's in-depth investigation into sightings of the legendary Sasquatch reminds us

just how small and defenseless we are beyond the safety of our living rooms. A word to the wise; if you're going to call-in a giant ape using a recording of a crying infant, make sure you're wearing your brown pants!"

- Max Hawthorne, author of the bestselling *Kronos Rising* series.

"I've listened to Shannon LeGro's podcast for years now, and I'm so stoked that she's finally put some of these stories down in print. It's Shannon's passion for this subject, her countless witness interviews, and her time spent in the field that make her one of today's go-to personas in the world of Sasquatch research. I'm sure it will come as no shocker to her fans—her book is fantastic. The encounters she's selected are awesome. Readers ranging from newcomers to the topic all the way to the 'Bigfoot Pros' will be informed, entertained, and at times, terrified. Yes, folks, it turns out she's just as good with a pen as she is the mic, and I for one hope this book is her first of many."

- Judd Lormand, actor (*SEAL Team, Jack Reacher: Never Go Back*)

INTRODUCTION

I often get asked why I became so interested in the subject of Sasquatch. I really can't answer that question simply, as I can't trace it back to an exact time and place, but it's fair to say my fascination goes well beyond just that topic alone. I have what can only be described as a hunger to explore and uncover all the unknown, those not readily explained things that cohabitate with us and for some manifest before their eyes.

This hunger for knowledge has taken me far and wide, from searching for Sasquatch across many states while filming the documentary ON THE TRAIL OF BIGFOOT, to investigating the notoriously haunted Fox Hollow Farm in Indiana and conducting research on Mothman in Point Pleasant, West Virginia. I've chalked up many miles, have found some evidence, but uncovering definitive proof has eluded me; yet I'll never tire or give up.

As of the publication of this book, I've

been hosting and producing the popular podcast *iNTO THE FRAY* since September of 2015. My show has two purposes. The first is to showcase experts and renowned researchers covering all topics in the paranormal and cryptid community. The second purpose, and one that I believe in my heart is the most important, is to provide a safe harbor for the many who have had encounters with such things as demons, Sasquatch, Dogmen, shadow people, UFOs, you name it. On my show they can open up and share their personal stories without judgment or fear of repercussion. For far too long they have felt marginalized, outcast, ridiculed and some harassed simply because they have come up against something they can't explain.

After mentioning all of this, I still haven't answered *why* I do what I do. Why have I dedicated my life to pursue these answers? Why do I tirelessly explore, knowing that I may never find the truth? To answer these questions I'll need to take you back to when I was twelve and to the beautiful mountain setting surrounding Cedar Mountain in Duck

Creek Village, Utah.

My father had a cabin in Duck Creek Village, a tiny hamlet nestled near Brian Head Ski Resort and five hours from our house in Las Vegas. If you're familiar with Duck Creek today, you'll know how quaint it is; back then it was simply one very small general store, a bait shop, six little rental cabins, and a hotel that always seemed to be under construction.

During this time in my life, we spent a considerable amount of time in Duck Creek. Our days would be filled with hiking, fishing, target practice with pellet guns, and one of my favorite pastimes as a kid...riding my four-wheeler. On most days we could be found traversing the trails and dirt roads on our four-wheelers up until way past sundown. Just up from Duck Creek was a steep graded dirt road that led to the privately owned cabins that sparsely dotted the landscape. The dirt roads crisscrossed the entire area, and with hardly any vehicle traffic to be concerned about, you could pretty much ride unencumbered.

The particular day in question was bright and sunny, not a cloud dotted the intensely blue sky, and the moderate temperature required only a light jacket. We would frequently ride without our helmets on, not the brightest thing to do, but it was often the case. This day was no different. It was midmorning and my brother and stepbrother were riding in front of me a little ways, not because I couldn't keep up, nope, it was because I hated getting dust in my eyes.

To say we were going fast would be a lie, we were hauling ass. With the throttles of our machines opened up, we sped down a long and straight road we knew very well. This was living and I loved it.

I caught a glimpse of something to my right. I glanced over and saw something running parallel to me about thirty feet in the forest. I kept looking and to my shock saw four human-shaped black silhouetted figures. The sun was casting through the trees, yet its rays didn't affect these figures, as if the light couldn't or didn't reflect or wasn't able to shine on them. It's hard to explain, but these six-foot-tall figures are the only objects I've ever seen devoid of light. It was as if they were animated cutouts from the blackest cloth you could ever imagine. What was even more startling and frightful was these things kept pace with me; their arms and legs moved with ease as they traversed through the forest without disturbing even a leaf or branch. Fear rose in me as I wondered if they'd look my way. Would they be faceless voids, similar to their bodies, or would I see a monstrous expression? I didn't want to know, and thankfully I didn't have to, as they kept their gaze ahead. I watched them for what I estimated to be a count of five, but I'll say now, it seemed like an eternity. I set my gaze back on the road in front of me to check my path of travel, then looked back, thinking they'd be there, but they were gone.

As I sit and type this, being the investigator I am now, I wish I could say I slowed down, stopped, or went back, but I didn't. I pushed my machine as fast as it would go, until I caught up with my brothers. When I reached them, I wasn't hysterical, but was visibly upset. They knew something was wrong when I said I wanted to go back to the cabin. As kids, the cabin was a place to sleep, nothing more, as our lives were outdoors. My brief encounter not only affected my time there, as I didn't ride again for almost a week, terrified of what I would see with a simple glance into the woods; it altered my life. Those five seconds changed my entire view of the world.

I shared with my father what I had seen. He told me it was probably just military men conducting training exercises. Unless these men were outfitted with some sort of amazing technology for Superman-like running speed, and a 'black as night' starter kit, those were not men, military or otherwise.

Those five seconds have been the only unexplained thing I've ever seen with my own eyes, and it is *the* reason I do this work. As scared as I was, it created this insane drive and questions, so many questions. What were they? Why were they there? Why did I see them when I did? It's too late for me to turn back; I'm in the hunt not just to find the answers to those questions but all things unexplained. This takes me to this book.

Some say the recent search for Sasquatch or Bigfoot officially began on September 21, 1958, when journalist Andrew Genzoli of the *Humboldt Times* featured a letter from a reader about loggers in northern California. The reader stated that loggers had discovered mysterious large footprints. Genzoli thought the letter fun, so he played along by stating in his column, which ran alongside the letter, *'Maybe we have a relative of the Abominable Snowman of the Himalayas.'* What Genzoli didn't know, and to his surprise, was the letter would ignite an interest and fascination in readers. The response was so good that he and fellow *Humboldt Times* journalist Betty Allen published follow-up articles about the footprints. In one of those follow-up articles they reported the name loggers had given the so-called creature whose tracks were becoming popular, that name was Bigfoot.

While America became transfixed on Bigfoot in 1958, history shows us that talk of a creature or 'wild man' living in the wilds of North America wasn't new. Native Americans as well as early American settlers long detailed stories and tales of hairy, giant, upright, human/apelike beings living in the woods. In fact, many cultures around the world have such folklore. For as many cultures have their stories, they also have their own unique names for the creature, with one becoming renowned, and that name is Sasquatch. The name Sasquatch is taken from the Sts'Ailes people of Chehalis, a First Nation people whose territories are in British Columbia, Canada.

Some in the modern age have described Sasquatch as a gentle creature, while others describe him as fierce and something to be feared. During my time conducting research and hosting my show, I have listened to many share their accounts. Some of these, while startling, provide evidence that Sasquatch can simply be curious and doesn't harm people; while others detail violent and threatening altercations. It is these particular stories I have compiled into this book for you to enjoy and use as a cautionary tale for when you journey into the woods.

I want to thank you for being here. You're about to take an intense trip, one filled with terrifying personal eyewitness encounters with the elusive Bigfoot, so buckle up.

And finally to my loyal podcast listeners and fans. For years I've taken you into the fray, together we've explored the unknown, the mysterious, the strange, and the bizarre. You have been my companions as we seek to find answers, yet if we never do, the journey itself has been the price of admission and well worth it. Now come with me as we again depart, but this time go...beyond the fray.

BOUNDARIES CROSSED

*L*ike many people who have had experiences with Sasquatch, David has been afraid to ever disclose, much less ever mention, to family or friends the terrifying encounter he had with the elusive creature, for fear of being mocked or ridiculed.

David's encounter can only be described as terrifying, and as you read his own words, you'll see this to be true. I'll finish with this: he had always wanted an encounter with Sasquatch and was willing to do anything to have it. But as you'll see, we should sometimes be careful what we ask for, because we just might get it.

***

As a kid, I was always more interested in

things like UFOs, ghosts, Bigfoot, things like that. Probably one of the biggest mistakes my mom ever made was giving me a copy of *The Amityville Horror* at a very young age, probably too young to have been appropriate reading; but regardless, that started my interest in all things paranormal. I remember watching a show when I was a little kid. I forget the exact name of it, but it was the first time I saw the Patterson-Gimlin film. As my young eyes watched the Sasquatch walk along the creek bed, I became hooked. From that point on I studied whatever I could find, watched everything I could get my hands on, which was limited for a kid in the 1970s because the only resources were libraries and such.

My passion for Bigfoot did have its limits though and eventually died out as I went into my teen years. In high school, I replaced the paranormal with music and whatever else was hip for the average teenager. However, as I entered my twenties, the interest in the mysterious and unknown rekindled in me. It was like an old friend whom you only see every now and then, but when you speak, you pick up right where you left off no matter how long it's been. I have to admit that what helped usher back my keen awareness and curiosity was a coincidence, a chance meeting, a crossing of paths, to be more exact, with a gentleman who was pretty well known in the Bigfoot research community. He and I hit it off almost immediately, almost like we've known each other our whole lives.

While we had become friends, he also took on the role of a teacher or mentor of sorts. He taught me all he knew concerning Sasquatch, never leaving a detail out. We spent many hours in the woods, covering all that I needed to know about how to study and compile research. One thing that he told me, and I had no reason to believe otherwise, was that the creature was nothing more than a gentle giant, that it didn't mean us any harm. I'd read of a few encounters that had been described as violent, but I was led to believe that this was extremely rare. Sasquatch was merely a gentle, kind and curious creature, a sweet denizen of the forest. I was told that as long as I was respectful, no harm would ever come to me. Well, I've since changed that opinion, and below will detail the events that led up to my fateful day.

It was 2001, and on an excursion into the woods, my mentor and I were out to research an area that was known by some to have a significant amount of activity. As we hiked back to one of the spots, we stopped to take a break. I pulled out a map. I always took topo maps with me; you can never be too careful when you're out in the wilderness.

Seeing the map in my hands, he took it from me and, using a marker, circled an area that was only a couple of hundred yards off a particular trail that had been marked earlier. He gave me a serious look and said, "Don't ever go here."

Not having seen him often with such a

serious look, I replied, "All right, I won't." My curiosity was heightened, so I asked, "Why is that?"

"Well," he replied with a pause to gather his thoughts, "I believe this is where they live."

I knew what that meant. The other areas were parts they roamed, hunted, etcetera. The circled area was their home, a place they could feel safe. I was still curious, so I asked him, "What makes you believe that?"

"I've had a few encounters there, and they've all been with younger ones or juveniles."

"All right. I will never go there," I said, although the desire to go was burning in me; plus I'm not a fan of being told I can't do something.

He shot me a hard look, knowing I was a rebel at heart.

"Okay, I'll never go there," I relented as I picked up on his body language. However, deep down I knew I was coming back and that

I'd have to do it alone.

Upon returning home, I planned my trip back. Since I only lived six hours away, that made it easy too. I told my wife I was going on a business trip, which wasn't a stretch, as I often did for my work.

The morning came for my lone trek to the forbidden area. I remember the day like no other; in fact, I often can't get it out of my thoughts. It was fall, but the cool chill of autumn hadn't taken hold yet. My need to go outweighed my normal precautions for hiking and exploring the wilderness. I literally broke every rule as far as safety goes, with the biggest one being that I told no one where I was going, and I mean that—not a soul knew.

I arrived, parked my car, and set out on what I estimated would be a forty-five-minute to an hour hike to get to the area where I *wasn't* supposed to go. My plan for the day was to just go there and poke around a little, see what I could see; essentially what I'm saying is I didn't even prepare for the hike and went without many items I normally take. I think I had a bottle of water, a couple of things to eat—light snacks but nothing major.

I arrived into the area, found a place to sit with a vantage point, and decided to just see what would happen. I recalled that I didn't see any signs, the things we usually look for while doing research. As time ticked away with nothing happening, I thought to myself, "Well, I'll hang out for a little while longer."

I can't recall how much time went by but enough without anything happening to get bored. I thought about leaving, but I couldn't because I had devoted my time to this, but the idea that if I stayed, I would finally get what I so wanted, and that was to see or experience Sasquatch firsthand. As it was fall, evening began to approach early. It was then I decided to stay the night. I knew it would be scary, but I figured it was too late to walk out, so I settled in for the long night. My plan was to get up at the crack of dawn, hike back, and be home before anyone really missed me. I sat back and got as comfortable as I could. The weight of fatigue soon overwhelmed me, and before I knew it, I was asleep.

Sounds of movement jogged me from my slumber. I lay there listening and straining to see. It wasn't pitch black but dark to the point where you almost can't see your hand in front of your face. Again, I heard something moving. It sounded large, very large. Aside from the sounds of movement, the woods were eerily quiet. My body tensed as the movement grew closer and closer. Then out of nowhere what I can only describe as hellish screams came from the darkness. These were screams I'd never heard before, and they shook me to the core. The comparisons to a woman being killed are accurate to a point; what I wasn't prepared for was the sheer volume and forcefulness. More screams came. These were from a different part of the woods, then another. It seemed as if they were now coming from every direction except from behind me, and the only reason I could figure was because I had positioned myself against a steep hill and faced out.

I had a flashlight, and as much as I wanted to turn it on, I didn't for a couple of reasons. First, I didn't want to see what was making this noise, and second, I didn't want whatever was making this noise to see me even though I assumed they already had.

My instinct was to get up and make a run for it; this was coupled by my thoughts screaming at me to do the very same thing. Using every ounce of courage I could muster, I got to my feet. My body was trembling uncontrollably, my breathing had increased, and my heart was pounding in my chest heavily.

Still the screams kept coming with ever increasing intensity. I took two steps to my right because only fifteen feet ahead of me was the trail that would lead me out.

Another scream bellowed from close in front of me. This time I actually felt it like the concussion you may feel from standing in front of a row of speakers at a concert. I froze. I couldn't even take one more step as fear gripped me.

As my mind attempted to deal with the terror of the situation, I still managed to reason with myself, albeit barely. If I was going to survive, I needed to keep moving. I took a little sidestep, only to have the scream from whatever was close to me once more halt my escape. Whatever it was, it wasn't going to let me go. I surrendered and dropped to my knees. I was surrounded now; screams came from all directions. I plugged my ears and cried out, "I'm trying to go. I'm trying to go. I don't want to be here. I will go. I will go!"

Suddenly I remembered that no one knew where I was. I was alone, deep in the woods, surrounded by things that sounded like they wanted to kill me, and I had never told a soul where I was. It was then that I thought this had now become a life-or-death matter. Thoughts then came of how ironic my situation was. Friends of mine who made fun of me for being interested in this kind of topic, and even my own wife for that matter, thought it was a big joke. Now, the thing that everyone ridiculed as not being real was going to kill me, and no one was ever going to know.

I curled up on the ground and prayed that somehow I could be saved. Time crawled by. What was probably a minute felt like an eternity.

As the screams kept coming, I fired back with a pleading tone, "I want to get out of here. If you let me get out of here, I will go, I will go!" All I could figure was that my mentor had been correct, his advice sound as it pertained to this being their home, their safe place, and I was the invader.

I really can't tell you how long I lay there, but finally I made up my mind that I needed to flee, but should I run? I thought. Everyone always says the worst thing you can do is run because you instantly become the prey and they become the predator. There was also another reason not to just get up and sprint away in a panic, and that was the trail ran along some pretty steep gorges and was rocky. Just one poorly placed footfall and I could trip and break a leg or, worse, fall to my death. Knowing I needed to do something, I began to crawl on my hands and knees.

As I inched towards the trail, the screams kept coming; what's incredible is they had never stopped since they began. I could also hear movement, heavy movement of something big, very big, close to me in between the infrequent pauses of the screams. I was no longer deterred though; if I was going to die, I'd at least die trying to get out of there.

It took what felt like forever to cover the short distance to the side trail then down it another one hundred or so yards to the main trail. All the while the screams and heavy movement kept sounding around me. When I reached the main trail, I was tempted to get up, turn on my flashlight, and sprint, but I resisted. I did, however, get to my feet and start to walk. I'm not ashamed to say that I was in tears. Actually it was worse than that, I was sobbing, fearful that I'd never make it out. It was then that I felt the nip of cold in the air, as my clothes were drenched from sweat. I knew I had a solid forty-five-minute to an hour hike to go under ideal conditions from where I was, and that it would take even longer in the dark.

With each footfall I took, I could hear that something was pacing me to either side not fifteen yards away. My mentor had taught me how to know if someone or something was pacing you. He said to stop abruptly and listen. No matter how closely something was trying to match your steps, they wouldn't be able to accurately time it and, hence, would give themselves away. I did this a few times and confirmed without a doubt there was something out there.

The screams eventually stopped, only to be replaced by something that I can only define as more creepy. The only way I can describe it is by saying it sounded like chattering. All around me I heard it. I got the impression they were talking back and forth while still following me. My head swiveled around frantically, looking to see if I could see one, not because I wanted to, no, only to make sure they hadn't finally decided to charge me. However, the dimly lit night and the thick trees prevented me from seeing anything.

I finally reached the last portion of the trail; it was a steep and rocky slope that dead-ended into the parking lot. It was there that I ran. Down the hill I sprinted without regard for my own safety, as I knew I was close, so very close to my car. I exploded out of the trailhead; ahead of me was my car just as I had left it. With my hands shaking uncontrollably, I managed to unlock the car, get inside and start it. I put the car into gear and smashed my foot against the accelerator and tore out of the parking lot.

As I drove to the hotel I had previously booked, all I could think was that I had survived. I couldn't stop crying; tears streamed down my cheeks. I made it to the hotel, checked in, and went to my room. There I locked the door, closed the blinds, and continued to sob. I was a mixed bag of emotions and contradictions. I felt like a coward because all this time, after hours and hours in the woods doing research, after wanting nothing more than to have a real encounter, I got one; but the reality was different than the fantasy. I had made a foolish assumption and it could have cost me my life.

I didn't sleep well that night, as was expected, and the next morning when I drove the long six hours home, all I could think was that I had made an incredibly foolish mistake. One, I had assumed that Sasquatch couldn't be threatening; all I can say is that while I had made it out, had I remained there, things more than likely would have taken a violent turn. It was apparent they didn't want me there. They perceived me as a threat, and if I had been persistent, I could have ended up a missing person. I then thought of my kids. What if I hadn't returned? Would they have been plagued with the thought that I had abandoned them? I had made the biggest mistake of my life and I regretted it.

Many years have separated me from that moment deep in the woods alone at night, but the memory still lives in me so clear, so vivid as if it happened just hours ago. It took me years to finally go back into the woods. Even now I'm haunted if I do, always looking over my shoulder at any sound, no matter how faint. My thirst to have an encounter with Sasquatch has left me, I fear, permanently scarred. However, I do have to admit something that will sound odd, and that is, there have been a few times since then that I've contemplated being able to have another encounter. I know it sounds sick, but I quickly come back to my senses.

To those of you who long for your chance to meet Sasquatch and who believe the stories that they're nothing but peaceful and gentle creatures know that I no longer hold that view. Yes, you can say they let me go that night, but if I had stayed, if I had resisted their display of power, how far would they have gone to expel me from their home? If my story doesn't cause you pause, and you're determined to go find these creatures, go prepared, and never go alone.

TWO HUNTERS

A large number of stories I've heard come from hunters, which makes sense. These are people who spend a considerable amount of time in the woods, sometimes alone. Imagine being isolated when an animal unlike anything you've seen comes into view through your scope; this wouldn't be an ideal situation to be in.

In this harrowing encounter we'll hear from Kris. He'll show us that we can encounter Sasquatch at any age and that it appears the creature seems to know what a rifle is.

***

It's hard to believe that it's been twenty-nine years, but it has. I was twelve, and for the first time I was being allowed to go deer hunting. This was meaningful, as I was now being considered a man in the family, someone who could put meat on the table, so to speak.

The hunting trip took me to a two-hundred-acre parcel my family owned in Wisconsin. There I'd be hunting with my father, uncle and cousins. I was no stranger to the property, as I'd pretty much spent every summer of my childhood there.

My cousin was just as excited about my first deer hunting trip as I was, so upon my arrival, he took me out to the woods to show me something unusual.

He asked, "Wanna see something weird?"

I replied, "Yeah."

He picked up a big stick, swung and whacked a tree hard. He repeated this several times.

I wasn't sure what he was doing until I heard a whack sound in the distance. At first I thought it was an echo. He handed me the stick and told me to try. Like him, I whacked the tree several times then waited. Just like before, I got a response far off in the woods. I'll admit, I didn't know what any of that meant, and in some ways I thought it was kind of cool.

My cousin then let out a yelp. Seconds later, something responded.

Again, I didn't know what to think about any of what he'd showed me, and before long we went back towards the cabin. I was fascinated by what could be responding to our whacks and yelps. Unable to get the odd incident out of my mind, I went back out to the same spot later. I picked up the branch I'd used before, swung and whacked the tree. Like before a response came back, but this time from a different part of the property and closer.

When I think back, I don't ever recall hearing about or knowing people who did tree knocks or vocalizations. It was apparent my cousin knew about it, but I was oblivious; heck, I didn't even know what Bigfoot was at that time.

Confused, I brought it up to my uncle, who was a man of few words. He simply told me to stop knocking on trees, and mumbled a name I wasn't familiar with. I shrugged it off and went about the rest of my day. What's odd is it wasn't until much later in my life did I hear that name again, this time from a prominent Bigfoot researcher, Coonbo Baker.

That night I was told where I'd be hunting. They were going to stick me way out at the far end of the property. A place I had been told to avoid before because of how remote it was and that I could get stuck back there due to the bogs and creeks. Looking back now, I do find it ironic I was stuck in the one place I was always told to stay away from.

The morning came and it was chilly. My uncle took me out and dropped me off. Before he left, he instructed me to stay put and that he'd come to get me at the end of the day. I nodded and went on my way.

This part of the two hundred acres was

much different than any other part. In fact, the whole atmosphere changed back there. It went from hardwoods to really thick brush, high grass and, like I mentioned before, bogs and creeks.

I went to an old willow tree, which held a rickety and aging tree stand. I put my foot on the first step, applied pressure, and sure enough, the first step broke. I thought to myself, *Great*. In order for me to reach the second step, I'd have to go back and make a running jump for it. Being twelve has its disadvantages, and height was one of them for me at the time.

I took a few steps back and went for it. I easily made the second step, although I was a bit nervous that it would break too, which would send me to the ground, crashing hard. This old tree stand wasn't very sturdy to begin with, as they'd used what appeared to be any old scrap of wood. Using every ounce of caution, I scaled up and took a seat.

Time ticked away and a chill began to

settle in me. Not a chill from fright but because I had been motionless, like a good hunter should be. It was a cloudy day and the warm rays of the sun were being hidden.

More time ticked away, and I knew I was doing a good job of being still, as every squirrel and bird came close, oblivious that I was even there.

The sun crept towards the horizon. The day was getting away from me, yet I'd not seen a deer. I suspected the shooting hours had passed and that my uncle would show up at any time. Patiently I waited, and waited and waited.

Dark wasn't far off and still my uncle hadn't come to get me. I grew concerned and knew I had two choices. I could continue to wait or get down and head back by myself. As I made up my mind on what to do, I took notice that everything around me had gotten very quiet. Fear suddenly took hold of me. I had felt it before in my life but not to this level or intensity. My eyes darted around and looked for the squirrels or birds that had populated the woods around me all day, only to find that they had gone. I couldn't see anything around me, yet I knew I wasn't alone, that something was out there.

The fear kept rising, but why? I still hadn't seen anything. Regardless, my senses screamed at me to go, run, get out of there. I knew that something wasn't right, but I just couldn't put my finger on it. The sun was sinking and it was getting darker by the second. I now knew that no one was coming to get me and that I was going to have to make a go of it on my own. I got ready to get out of the stand, then did everything you shouldn't do with a .30-30 lever-action rifle when climbing out of a stand. I half-cocked the rifle because I knew I'd be the most vulnerable and exposed as I climbed out of the stand and down the willow tree. I couldn't see much of anything around me, yet I couldn't shake this feeling that something was there, close by.

Slowly I navigated down the tree, taking

care with each foot placement until I reached the last step. From there I planned on jumping. Without a second's hesitation, I leapt. I hit the ground and quickly recovered. I got up and now I was facing down a path or what might have been an old deer trail. What little bit of light was left illuminated the open space in front of me. It was then I spotted something rise just off the trail to my right about thirty feet. It towered like nothing I'd ever seen before. I guess now that it stood over seven feet or maybe eight.

My body tensed, and the fear that I thought was elevated already rose to almost sheer terror. Instinctually I cocked the hammer fully back on the rifle and threw it into my shoulder. Just as I did that, whatever this thing was raised one leg, stretched it out and placed it on the opposite side of the trail. It now straddled both sides, its massive frame focused on me and my rifle.

I have to laugh now, because believe it or not, I began to think about hunter safety. *Know your target and beyond,* my mind screamed at me for just a brief second before I hollered back, *Know your target? I don't know what I'm even looking at!* Whatever it was could only be described as massively tall, around seven to eight feet tall, and wide, its shoulder spanning feet across the trail.

The fading light of the day shined from behind it, making it impossible to make out good detail, but the outline was crystal clear. I made out that it was standing on two feet, had legs, arms and a head. I could also make out hair or fur or whatever you want to call it. I thought to myself, *What am I seeing?* With the butt of the rifle in my shoulder, I put the scope on it and looked through. My scope was low powered with a yellow filter, which illuminated everything a bit more, but still not enough to clearly make out what I was seeing. I placed the reticle of my scope on the vitals, placed my finger on the trigger, and stood ready to unload everything I had if it made one move towards me. The entire time I thought that I was going to die, that this was it. I still couldn't make out any facial features of the creature because the light came from behind it, but I just knew this thing could easily kill me. With all the slack taken out of the trigger, I was ready to fire, but it didn't move. Both of us were at a standstill, our gazes fixed on the other.

I couldn't say how long we stood staring each other down, but it felt like forever. Then without notice, it leapt to the right from where it stood. All I heard now was crashing as it fled. A minute later there was silence. I then saw something farther down the trail; it was the silhouette of a deer. It dawned on me that I had come in between this thing and its meal. I assumed it must be mad at me, so I did the worst thing possible, I turned and ran.

With each step, my heart pounded to the point I swore it would explode. My vision narrowed, which made it harder to get a good view.

To my right, the direction the thing had

gone, I heard movement. I now thought this thing was going to circle around and come for me. I got up, swung my rifle around, and again readied myself to fire, but nothing was there. Without wasting another second, I pivoted and raced off again down the trail.

I don't know how long it took me, but I did finally make it back to camp. Not a second after my arrival, my uncle and everyone began to haze me. They could tell I had been spooked, with someone joking that I looked like I'd seen a ghost. What they didn't know was I had seen something far worse.

I asked my uncle why he hadn't come to get me, and he replied that he had tried but couldn't find me. I didn't know what to believe. All I knew was I was glad to have made it out of there alive, as I was sure my demise was certain. I rushed inside the cabin with my rifle, only to have my uncle remind me he didn't like weapons inside, only because he said they sweated from the change in temperature. I told him I would clean it and went inside.

I wiped the rifle down and carefully hid it, loaded, under my bed and slid my sheath knife underneath my pillow.

While I had made it back, I couldn't calm down and didn't feel safe. A large window overlooked my bed, and all I could imagine was awakening to that thing hovering over me just outside the thin panes of glass. I could see it crashing through the walls, taking hold of me and, well, that would be it. Needless to say, I didn't sleep an hour that night. Come morning, everyone was up, and the last thing I wanted to do was go back out there. I hadn't told anyone what had happened, but they knew something was wrong. However, that didn't stop them from hazing or making fun of me; it's just what they did.

I told my dad I didn't feel good, that I had gotten too cold the day before, so maybe I could take the stand closest to the cabin. My plan was to bag a deer as fast as I could and get the hell out of there. I knew this was my only way out.

I arrived to my new stand, and believe it or not, I got a deer rather quickly. I was excited, mainly because I could now head home. Then I was told there were more tags to fill, so I was to help drive deer to the others. My heart sank; I felt defeated and terrified because I'd have to be back out there.

With my hands white-knuckled on my rifle, I walked through the woods. My head swiveled back and forth every time I heard a sound. With each crack of a branch or crunch of leaves, I snapped my head with the expectation of seeing a monster pop up, only to see a deer or squirrel. I made it through the drive, which ended the hunt. Hours later we were headed home.

Looking back now, I think it's fair to say my life was on the line that day, and the one thing that saved me was my old .30-30 lever-action rifle. I can still feel it angrily looking at me, both of us locked in a standoff, with neither committed to act.

I went back to the property a few years later but made sure I never went to that part of the property again. I figured that was his territory and also figured he was probably still mad at me.

As the years passed, I tried to convince myself that I hadn't really seen what I saw, that it all was the wild imagination of a twelve-year-old. I dared never mention it to my family for fear they'd mock or ridicule me, so I held in the fear from that day, never uttering a word to another until now. Even in my best efforts to wipe my memory of that time or imagine it was something else, I always regressed. I don't ever think I'll forget that day; like so many others I've heard tell their tale, it's something that becomes seared into your memory.

I still venture back into the woods, but now I go with the knowledge there are creatures there that could do us considerable harm. When I go, I'm always armed. Whatever those things are, they know what a rifle is, and

I believe they also know what it's capable of. My rifle saved me that day twenty-nine years ago, I know this without question. I also know that on that day there were two hunters in those woods.

.

THE CRIES OF A BABY

*T*he next story was given to me from Derek Randles. He, along with Shane Corson, Dave Ellis and others, run the Olympic Project, in Washington State. They are an association of dedicated researchers, investigators, biologists and trackers committed to documenting the existence of Sasquatch through science and education. Through comprehensive habitat study, DNA analysis and game camera deployment, the Olympic Project's goal is to obtain as much information and empirical evidence as they can, with hopes of being prepared when and if species verification comes to fruition. Their studies are conducted in a noninvasive manner with respect and sensitivity to the probable habitat they believe the species inhabits.

Derek's story is unique in the manner of how he was able to draw the creature to him. As you'll see, this new approach, while novel and some *would say creative, almost ended in a way that could have been deadly.*

***

My name is Derek Randles, I'm fifty-four years old and live in Tahuya, Washington. I am the co-founder of the Olympic Project in Washington State and have been researching Sasquatch since a sighting and encounter I had in 1985.

The story I'm sharing happened in the late '90s, I believe it was 1998. I had seen renowned anthropologist Grover Krantz on television discussing Bigfoot, and was so intrigued that I made a trip to his house in Edmonds, Washington, to pick his brain. To be honest, I invited myself over. At that time, Grover, I believe, was a professor at Washington State University in Pullman. I'd always wanted to talk to him about many things, but one major question I had was about ways he imagined one could attract or lure a Sasquatch in the field.

We sat down and talked. I asked many pointed questions. One of them was where, in his opinion, was the best place to encounter a Sasquatch. He didn't hesitate and answered, "McCall, Idaho." I found that interesting, and it made sense, as McCall was and still is a remote part of Idaho. Right after, I asked him, "If you went to such a place, what, in your opinion, could you do to possibly attract a Sasquatch or lure one to your position?"

He chuckled and said, "Well, maybe a baby crying."

I replied, "Wow, that's interesting."

He went on to describe how if I made a tape of a baby crying, got to a remote location where I knew they existed, played the tape, and if the circumstances were right, maybe I could draw a Sasquatch in.

As I sat and listened to him, a light bulb went off in my head.

I returned home, and the very next night, using a cassette recorder, I recorded my young son, who happened to cry a lot. I got a good bit of him crying, then turned it into a loop tape, which I could play continuously until the cassette ran out.

Armed with what I thought was an ingenious idea, I headed out for an area called Burnt Fork in the Blue Mountains. I had heard about Burnt Fork because it was where Paul Freeman, a Sasquatch researcher in the area at that time, had investigated sightings and encounters some hunters had with Sasquatch. Knowing it was a remote area, I figured if I was going to find a Bigfoot, this would probably be one of the best places to go.

I drove to the area, put on my backpack, and started out on my hike. I have to say that this area is a vast remote place. I hiked for approximately six hours in one direction until I got down to the bottom of a ravine. I looked around and thought this was perfect. As far as I could surmise, this was close to the area where the hunters had had their encounter the hunting season prior.

It was getting late in the day, so I

immediately set up where I'd be waiting. I found a large tree approximately sixty feet above the bottom of the ravine, with a good and clear vantage point. A creek ran through the base of the ravine, and the area around it was mostly open except for brush that sat on the opposite side, which stood about eight to ten feet. I took off my pack and settled in.

Armed with a Sony NightShot camera that had a generation three night-vision monocular, which married up to the front of the camera, I was prepared to record anything I encountered or that happened. I had gotten the camera from Jeff Meldrum, professor of Anatomy and Anthropology at Idaho State University, one or two years before when he'd invited me to join the North American Ape Project to do some investigations for that group. The camera at the time was really state-of-the-art stuff. To this day, it's really an amazing piece of equipment.

From my position, I looked around and thought that I had found a good spot. It didn't take long for it to start getting dark, and it was then that I had my first reservations about what I was doing. Many questions soon came. Was this a good idea? Was this a bad idea? Was I stupid? I pushed those questions out of my mind temporarily and waited. Quickly it got very dark. I was pretty tired from the hiking and the drive up earlier that day. I was hoping I could stay awake for a while to see if this was going to work and was worth it.

Before long it was pitch black. I couldn't see anything, but I could hear the creek running down in the ravine below. I finally decided to do what I had set out to do, so I turned my cassette player on. I immediately noticed the acoustics from my particular spot were really good. As my son's cries carried through the air, I could tell it was going a long distance. This was good because if I was going to lure something in, it needed to go far. In fact, as I sat and listened, I was impressed that the crappy recorder I was using worked so well.

After probably an hour, it was getting more and more difficult to listen to my son crying over and over and over again. I was also starting to get a bit of a headache. I let it go for a bit longer, then did a battery change and fired it back up.

More time went by, I can't recall how long, but it was getting late, and I was having a tough time staying awake. I really was ready to turn off the crying because my headache was getting worse, but I decided to hang on a little longer. I figured I'd come all this way, I should take it as long as possible before quitting.

Suddenly on the range opposite of where I was sitting, a loud crash sounded. I perked up; any signs of fatigue vanished in that moment. I reached into my pack out of an abundance of caution and pulled out a pistol. I always pack a firearm when I go into the wilderness, and this wasn't unlike any other time. So I got out my pistol and made myself ready.

My son's cries were still going, as I hadn't

SHANNON LEGRO & G. MICHAEL HOPF

stopped playing the recorder, but the crashing on the opposite ridge was also still there. Five minutes or so went by, and the crashing was still echoing through the ravine, but it was now getting louder as whatever was making the noise advanced towards me or, I should say, towards the sounds of my son's cries.

It was then that I started to seriously evaluate and question what the hell I was doing out there and, to be honest, my judgment. I was a long way out in the woods, a good six to eight hours away from anyone, and vulnerable. I was also trying something that as far as I knew had never been tried before.

As the crashing got louder and louder, I grew more tense and nervous. I got the camera ready to start filming, but I also had my pistol too, just in case.

The sounds of crashing grew louder. I was now beyond just tense, my hands began to shake, and real fear began to grip me. It then dawned on me that whatever was coming wasn't really coming for me, but to the cries…it was coming to the cries of my infant son!

My mind raced. I asked myself, "Is this Bigfoot? Is it two Bigfoot? Is it a bear? What is it?" The sounds grew in volume, as did my fear. At this point, I couldn't stop questioning my poor judgment.

Like a locomotive, whatever it was had now reached the flat part of the ravine and was coming towards the creek. I could now tell that it was on two feet, as I could hear the heavy and violent footfalls. If I could give an analogy, it sounded like a linebacker racing through the woods without regard for anything around it.

I was now hanging on to reality by a thread. I didn't know what to do. I was terrified—hell, I was frozen with fear, as there was zero doubt now this thing was running directly at me. All that was separating me from it was the creek and the brush that was probably about fifteen to twenty feet wide and about six to eight feet tall.

My fear now reached a fever pitch. By how loud it was now, I could have sworn it was almost on top of me. Unable to see my experiment through, I lost my nerve and shut the recorder off.

The crashing stopped almost instantly, as if it came to a skidding halt on the opposite side of the creek and brush line. And when I say skidding halt, I could swear I heard it slide. I probably didn't, but that's what it felt like at the time, like it just slid to a full stop.

The loud sounds of crashing were now replaced with deep, heavy, raspy breathing. In and out, it inhaled, then exhaled.

In my mind I thought, "Oh my God, this thing is ready to come through this brush." Only sixty feet separated me from this thing. All it needed to do was punch through the brush, head up the slope sixty feet, with nothing really in the way, and it would have had me dead to rights.

Doubts took over my troubled and

terrified mind. Right then and there I was officially done with doing research. I couldn't help but keep thinking how stupid I was, how dumb it was for me to even be there, so far out, unprepared both mentally and probably even physically to deal with what was standing on the other side of that creek breathing. I was freaked out and didn't know what to do.

In my trembling hands I clenched my pistol in one, and in the other held out the NightShot camera, hoping to see just a little bit. All the while, I was waiting on pins and needles for the thing to crash through the brush and come at me.

I can't recall exactly when, maybe it was around three to four minutes, but the sound of the breathing stopped, making it even more creepy. All I kept thinking was the thing was possibly stalking me now or, worse, would jump out of the darkness at me. I can't say it enough, I was freaked out beyond compare. In my mind, I kept yelling at myself about how stupid I was and what a dumb decision this was to be alone and about eleven or twelve miles in.

I knew I had a decision to make: do I get up and make a run for it or just remain still? I opted for staying, so I waited and waited. I can't remember how long I sat there, quiet, my mind spinning, before my fatigue caught up with me; but the next thing I remember is waking to birds chirping and sunshine. I looked around, but nothing was there. The brush below looked as it did the night before, I could hear the creek running, and I was sitting in the same position I had been before I fell asleep.

The fear and apprehension I'd had were gone; sometime in my sleep they had melted away. I got to my feet and, with my sidearm on, headed down to the creek. I went through the thick brush line, emerged on the other side, and immediately found two very large impressions and quite a large disturbed trail coming up to that spot. That moment the reality struck me—those were Bigfoot tracks. I couldn't believe it, I just couldn't believe it. Then my mind shifted to what would have happened if I hadn't turned the recorder off. Would I be here today? Would that thing have torn me apart?

I quickly documented the tracks photographically, went back to the tree where I'd spent the night, gathered my gear, and began my long hike out of there. On my eight-hour hike back, I never encountered anything else, but I did go back and forth about my judgment concerning what I'd done and if I'd have a future with research.

Many years separate me from that moment, but I'll never forget it. I've processed it in my brain over and over and now realize just how overwhelmingly stupid and disrespectful it was. I know that sounds weird, but here I am using the cries of a baby to lure something in, but what I was really doing was toying with its emotions. Whatever I put it through wasn't fair or right. I'm not proud of that moment, not one bit. I feel ridiculous, and without a doubt it was one of the stupidest things I've ever done.

I'm really glad I turned that tape off because, you know, I might not be here telling this story if I didn't. I don't know what it would have done, but I damn sure know what it was.

DOGMAN ON TEMPLE ROAD

*W*hen it comes to cryptozoology, much of the focus has been on Sasquatch, but there is another cryptid that some consider more terrifying. As if an encounter with the Big Guy wasn't scary enough? I'm referring to a Dogman. If you're unaware of what a Dogman is, let me briefly explain. A Dogman is described as an upright canid, and according to some, there are two types, a K9 type and a Type-3. The K9 is essentially an upright walking canine. The Type-3 is similar to a Sasquatch but with a muzzle instead of a flat face and claws on their hands and feet.

Sightings of these creatures can be traced all the way back to the 1800s. Some of the early documentation came from Wexford County,

Michigan, back in 1887 when two lumberjacks saw a creature that they described as having a man's body and a dog's head. Since then, encounters with this type of cryptid have been reported across the United States from rural parts to even urban centers, with many witnesses stating they felt a deep sense of dread, sometimes before the creature is even in view. Dogmen also seem to have a careless attitude towards being seen...even to the extent of stepping out of cover to allow the witness a full gaze of its truly imposing form.

The story below not only fits that bill but is credible, as it comes from none other than a judge, a man sworn to uphold the law and to tell the truth.

***

The story I'm about to tell happened when I was fifteen years old. It was shocking and so terrifying that it changed my life forever, and the memory of it still lives in me as if it happened just yesterday.

It was the third week of August 1985;

school would be starting soon and I was training for a 10K race that was held every year for a festival in town. I remember it was a hot August day with the temperature pushing close to a hundred degrees. I was supposed to run five miles, but due to the high temperatures, I put off my run until evening.

Running at night wasn't a big deal to me. I grew up on a farm in the country and wasn't scared of the dark. Often during my childhood I ran around at night, racing through cornfields, playing hide-and-seek, you name it; I was outside no matter the hour. So the concept of going for a long run down a country road in the dark wasn't something I was fearful of.

I had my route planned. I'd leave my house, run down the ditch of State Route 4 for about three hundred yards until I reached Temple Road, which dead-ended into it. From there I'd run down Temple Road until it intersected with State Route 98, this was the halfway mark, so from there the plan was to turn around and just come back.

Night came, it was around ten o'clock, and I headed out. There was enough moonlight to see, but it definitely wasn't a full moon. I got to the halfway mark at State Route 98, turned around, and started heading back. There wasn't much along Temple Road, just cornfields on one side and soybeans on the other, with small pockets of trees dotting the landscape and only a couple of farmhouses along that stretch of the road back then.

I was more than halfway done my run and it was going great. I was closing in on a crossroad, which meant I was only about a mile out from Route 4. On my left there was a pocket of trees, then the crossroad, which was Flickinger Road, and on the other side of that, a cornfield that stretched a mile all the way to Route 4. On my right just after the crossroad was a field of soybeans, which too stretched a mile.

It was at the wooded area where I sensed something was wrong. I don't know how to say it, but I just felt like something was off. It was enough of a feeling that I stopped running. The warm evening air felt a bit cool against my hot skin, and as I stood taking in deep breaths and looking around, I couldn't shake the feeling that I wasn't alone.

Movement suddenly came from the cornfield near the crossroad. I snapped my head in the direction of the sound and looked, but with the corn standing about six feet tall, I couldn't see anyone or anything. More sounds of movement came. This time I saw the corn moving, and I could tell by how many stalks were being disturbed that whatever it was, it was big. This instantly jolted me with fear, but only because I wasn't expecting to hear something while on my run. My first instinct was to assume it was a deer, and why? Because we had a huge deer population in Ohio, and I couldn't imagine it was anything else.

I pushed aside my initial fear and began to run again. Whatever was in the corn also began to run. What was odd was whatever was there was not running towards me, but was running *with* me, like through the corn and keeping pace with me. When I say pace, I mean it was running at my *exact* pace.

I looked over at the corn and saw that whatever was running alongside me was about four rows in from the edge of the field, making it impossible to see what it could be.

I stopped again, turned and looked, hoping to catch a glimpse, but only grew more fearful, as it too stopped the very second I did. I strained to see what it could be, but it wasn't moving an inch and was quiet. I knew then this wasn't usual behavior for a deer. The air around me was still, not a breeze of any kind, but the feeling, oh, the feeling was thick with a sense of dread. In the back of my mind, I knew deer didn't act like this, but I assumed it had to be a deer, although a very odd one, because what else could it be? Hoping to spook it, I hollered out, but nothing happened.

Unsure what else to do, I took off running

again, and sure enough, it ran too. Freaked that it was again pacing me, I stopped and it stopped. I was beyond concerned, I was terrified. My adrenaline was pumping and my mind was spinning about what it could be. By the amount of corn I saw moving when it was pacing me, it had to be bigger than a dog or coyote; and I knew there weren't bears in this part of Ohio. As I went through a list of animals large enough to make such a disturbance in the corn, only to come up with nothing, I began to tremble.

My heart pounded and the intense dread I felt was enough to make anyone go crazy. I was alone, engulfed by the dark of night, and something large was in the corn. I didn't know what it was or what was going on, but I did know that I wanted to get as far away from it as I could. I knew that I had three-quarters of a mile to go until I got to Route 4, and then a short few hundred yards to my house beyond that.

I didn't know what else to do except keep

running; but if I did, whatever it was would only keep pacing me; this meant I needed to change it up. I needed to not just run, I needed to run as fast as I could—I had to give it all I had. I was confident in my abilities, as I was a good runner and really fast. As I inhaled several deep breaths, I concocted a plan to sprint about three to four hundred yards, enough, I thought, to outpace and eventually put some distance between me and whatever the hell was in the corn still being eerily still and quiet. I figured there was no way this thing could see me, because I couldn't see it; and with the fully grown corn being an obstacle; it would have a difficult time keeping up...or so I thought.

I began a countdown in my head. As I ticked down, I readied myself for what felt at that moment like the run of my life. I bent slightly at the hip, leaned in and tensed my body.

*Ready, set, go...*I took off like I was being shot from a cannon. For a split second I felt like I'd be able to outrun this thing, but then…then I heard it. Like the other two times, it was pacing me. Whatever this damn thing was, it was keeping up with me even though it had to blast through the corn to do so.

I dug deeper and pushed harder. My pace increased, but it wasn't any good, as it kept matching mine—if I went faster, it went faster. I could feel my heart pumping hard and fast; I was giving all I had, but it wasn't enough.

I covered about three hundred yards and I could feel I was done, gassed, out of steam. Unable to keep going, I stopped; and like before, it stopped too. I now came to the horrifying conclusion that whatever was in the corn was not only faster than me, but there was no way it was a person. There was then and still is now no one who could run through the corn like it had. I don't care if you brought in an Olympian track star, they'd not be able to do it; it was impossible.

I stood in the road; a deep feeling of defeat washed over my trembling body. I had totally spent all my energy to get away from this thing and I'd failed. I took my eyes off the corn and stared down the long stretch of road that I still needed to cover. I was scared, alone, and still had a good half mile to go in order to reach Route 4.

The only thing close to me was an old abandoned farmhouse about a hundred yards down the road to my right. I recalled there had been an old tree in the front yard and quickly adjusted my plan. What I'd do now was carefully make my way there, climb it to the top, and wait until morning.

Armed with this new plan, I made my way slowly towards the tree. With every step I took, this thing moved too. I made it to the tree, and the second I looked at it, my heart sank, as there was nothing to grab a hold of, as the tree had been dehorned. I couldn't climb the tree, it was impossible, and once more I felt defeated.

As I stood staring at the tree, a terrifying realization came to me. Even if I made it the next half mile to Route 4, I'd have to turn left and possibly cross paths with whatever was there. I imagined making the turn and it, whatever it was, would come out and get me. I immediately pushed the fear out of my mind and focused on what I'd do next. I wasn't done yet; I wasn't going to just give up. I needed to keep going, but with going left not an option, I decided I needed to go right, and that was when it hit me. My good friend lived off Route 4 but in the opposite direction, which meant all I needed to do was make it to Route 4, turn right and race down about a hundred and fifty yards.

I thought about making a run for his house across the soybeans, but quickly dismissed the idea, as I feared I'd get tangled up in the soybean plants. No, I needed to keep pressing forward down Temple Road, but this time I'd go slow to conserve my energy for what I hoped would be my grand finale, a one-hundred-fifty-yard sprint to my buddy's house.

Not wasting another second in thought, I pivoted and began my long march towards the intersection of Route 4. Each step I took was matched by the thing in the corn. In my mind, a flurry of questions were flying around. *Is this thing baiting me? Is it stalking me? Is it just messing with me?* I didn't know what to think, all I knew was it still hadn't come out, but that fact didn't give me peace of mind because at any moment it could, and there was not a doubt in my mind that if it did, I'd be dead.

Route 4 came into view as a car barreled down it, the headlights illuminating the area for a brief moment. I readied myself for what I knew would be the run of my life, literally. More questions entered my already troubled mind. Would I look over my shoulder and see it? Did I want to look over my shoulder? Would it give chase? What was it? If I looked back, would doing so slow me down, or would looking back and seeing something awful scare me to the point that I'd freeze? In a snap decision I decided that when I took off, I wouldn't look back, I'd just hammer out the run and hope that it didn't come after me.

With less than twenty feet to go to the intersection, I picked up my pace and, of course, it matched me. I looked to my right, over the rows of soybeans, and didn't see any traffic. I craned my head to the left and saw a glow of lights shining over the tops of the corn. A car was coming and it posed me with another issue. *Do I stop and wait, or do I just make my move?*

I threw all caution to the wind and took off at full speed like I was coming out of the starting blocks for a hundred-meter dash. I cleared where the corn ended on my left, which allowed me to see Route 4 clearly. Down the road I spied a truck, but it was far enough away for me to safely cross.

I had sworn that I wouldn't look back, but I couldn't resist. I craned my head over my shoulder, and right at that moment I saw something exit the corn and stop. I can't recall how long I looked at it, but it was long enough to get a good look, and all I can say is the first thing that came to mind was the Egyptian God Anubis. I had no other frame of reference back then, nor was I aware of Dogmen much less Bigfoot. All I knew was it walked out, upright on two legs, and stood about six to seven feet tall; I could judge its height because its head was taller than the corn. It had a well-defined canine head, dark hair, and its build was similar to that of a greyhound, lean and muscular. It stood with its body postured like it was in a stance and its shoulders rolled forward. At the time it reminded me of how a linebacker stands ready for the ball to be snapped.

It turned its head and looked at me. By its stance and long arms positioned out in front of it, I presumed it was readying itself to pursue me. I faced forward and gave it all I had. I cleared a hundred yards with ease, cut across one yard and came up on the boundary of my buddy's backyard. In front of me was a chain-link fence, and I prayed the gate was open, but as I drew closer, I saw it was closed and most likely locked. I decided in an instant that I would jump the fence. Now, the fence wasn't too tall, but it was tall enough for me not to be able to hurdle it.

I reached it, grabbed hold of the top, which was just exposed and jagged metal, and threw myself over. As I flew over, a sharp edge of the fence gouged my side, but I didn't let it slow me down. I landed on the other side and could now see the swimming pool in front of me. I made a split-second decision and dove in, not thinking that it was the shallow end. My chest hit the bottom and I slid down to the deep end, which was about ten feet. I rolled onto my back, exhaled all my air, pinched my nose, and looked up.

I lay there; my body screamed with pain as my eyes darted around, looking for it to walk up and stare down on me in the pool. What must have been thirty seconds went by. Nothing showed up, no towering figure, no shadows cast down on me in the pool. Had I made it? Did it not follow me? Unable to hold my breath any longer, I swam to the surface, quickly looked around, but didn't see it anywhere. I swam to the edge and crawled out.

Frantic, I raced to the back sliding door of the house. I didn't know if it was locked or not. I grabbed the handle and pulled. The door flew open. I stepped through the vertical blinds that had been closed for privacy and into the house. What I didn't know was his parents were out of town, and what he wasn't expecting was anyone to suddenly appear, yet here I was.

My buddy jumped from his chair when I entered the living room. He wasn't just shocked to see me, he was also a bit embarrassed, as he'd been watching the Playboy Channel.

He peppered me with many questions, all of which I answered as best I could between heavy breaths. I finally regained my composure and told him what had happened and what I'd seen. At first he doubted me, assuming I'd seen something like a deer. I wouldn't waver; I knew what I'd seen; I knew what had just happened. Eventually he came around, and when he did, he too became scared.

After agreeing for me to stay the night, we locked all the doors and turned the lights out. The rest of the evening was spent walking around his house and peering out the windows, half expecting to see the Dogman lurking about outside.

The morning came and with it brought a sense of calm and relief; I had survived whatever that was I had seen, and I couldn't be happier. My buddy took me home, and I immediately told my father what had occurred. I didn't know what to expect from him, but he quickly dismissed my story. He told me that because I had gotten spooked, my mind had played tricks on me. Like I did with my buddy, I stood my ground and told him I knew what I had seen and that I hadn't imagined it. What's interesting though about my dad was that after my encounter, he never went outside at night without tucking a .38-caliber pistol into the back of his pants. That told me all I needed to know. He did believe me, but by admitting it, he probably thought it would have scared me more than I already was. I chalked up his dismissal as a way of him protecting me.

Much time has now separated me from that night, but the fear, that still remains in many ways. I've never run that stretch of road since, even during the daytime. I also never ran again at night, anywhere. I still live in the area, and no matter when I venture out at night, I usually have a weapon with me and I'm always on alert.

Years later I became aware of the term *Dogman*, and upon doing some research, I have no doubt that what I encountered that night was just that. I'm not afraid to tell anyone about what happened to me that night.

I know what happened and I know what I saw. My openness and transparency has no doubt resulted in some rolling their eyes or thinking that I imagined it; but I have met others who believe. These believers have showered me with theories of that night. Some say that a Dogman has the traits of a canine; those being that they run and hunt in a pack. They pointed out that maybe the one that paced me was simply driving me to others that were waiting. This thought has and still sends chills down my spine. What if I had decided to make a run for my house? Would the one that exited the corn have given chase, or were there others just on the other side of the road in the cornfield? I'll never know, but it gives me pause. I still don't know why it never came out of the corn before Route 4. Was it just toying with me?

I have replayed that night over and over again, and each time I imagine it coming after me, and what follows is my demise. It was faster than me, appeared much stronger, and without a doubt could have run me down and killed me; yet it didn't. Again, I don't know why it never came after me, I'm just happy that it didn't.

To those who may doubt the existence of a Dogman, I can tell you that they exist and there is plenty of open and remote land for them to call home. To those who scoff at a story like mine, I say that history has shown us many tales of strange creatures only for those creatures to eventually be discovered decades later by the scientific community. For me, it's only a matter of when, not if Dogmen are scientifically proven to exist; but if it doesn't happen in my lifetime, that's fine. I know what I experienced that night, and I know what I saw, as it's seared into my memory. So as a warning to those who are reading, Dogmen are out there, and if you're ever thinking of running late at night on Temple Road, don't.

SCARFACE

*S*o often when it comes to people's assumptions about Bigfoot, one is that these elusive creatures can only be found in the vast forests and wilderness of the Pacific northwest. However, I can tell you after many interviews with eyewitnesses that these creatures are found all across the United States, including near heavily populated areas like New York City. Our next story details such an encounter. It is not only a terrifying one, but serves as an example that just because you're on a hiking trail close to town, that doesn't mean you won't come face-to-face with a Bigfoot.

***

It was summer and I was thirteen years old. I was enrolled in a summer day camp in upper

New Jersey. This meant that on any given day we could be on a bus to the Pine Barrens, the Adirondacks and so forth. This day our destination was Bear Mountain State Park in New York. For those who aren't familiar, Bear Mountain is a New York State park located about fifty miles north of New York City and sits along the Hudson River. The park itself, which is about five thousand acres, feels remote even though it's not.

When I think back on that day specifically, I can't recall all that we did upon arriving at the park, but what happened later is burned into my memory. I know we went hiking, as that was something we did everywhere we went. I remember we had just hiked up a mountain, or hill for those who live out west, and near the top had taken a break for lunch.

At this time in my life I was trying to be a bad boy, i.e., smoking cigarettes and whatnot. Another kid and I took off from the group to go do just that, but in order to not get caught, we needed to be at a safe distance. We hiked through a patch of woods then went up a rocky outcrop and down the other side to a clearing. As we were traversing our route, we kept hearing something moving through the woods just above us. He nor I thought anything of it, we couldn't tell if it was walking on two or four legs, and we just assumed it was a deer or something. Again, our heads were focused on finding a safe place to light up.

When I think back on what happened next, it just goes to show how quickly things that seem so normal can turn to utter terror in an instant.

My friend and I were joking as we went. I stopped so I could light my cigarette, turned to face him, and just as I finished making my turn, I could see a look of shock stretched across his face. His unlit cigarette fell from his lips, and without a second's hesitation, he spun around and took off running. I instantly thought that he must have seen something like a bear, so I turned to see what had spooked him, only to discover that it wasn't a bear or any other animal I was familiar with but something out of a nightmare.

Towering over me, not ten feet away, was this huge gray-haired monster, for lack of a better word. Petrified in fear, I stood, my eyes fixed on its hips, as that was where my eye level was. At thirteen, I wasn't short for my age, but I also wasn't tall; but what stood in front of me was the tallest living bipedal creature I'd ever seen in my life. It's taken me years to come to grips with how big this thing was, and now I can confidently say that it stood about nine to ten feet tall.

In its enormous right hand, the creature held the remains of half a dog, a shaggy blonde Labrador, by its neck. The lower half of the dog was missing, I had no idea if it had eaten it or if that part had been discarded. But the half it did have appeared to have been ripped from the other. Dried blood clung to the dog's fur, and entrails hung out of the open carcass, telling me the dog had been dead for a while. What I found even more disturbing was what the creature held in its left hand. There dangling from its grip was a garment or blanket. It was hard to tell which, but it told me that it had encountered someone else before it had run into us. Which begged the question, where were they? Had it come upon someone walking their dog? Had it killed them and then ripped the dog in half? Where was it taking this half of the dog, back to others like it? My mind spun with so many questions and it screamed at me to do something besides stand there.

Filled with terror, my mind raced as to what I should do. I knew I needed to run, but I couldn't; I was frozen, unable to move. I had a clear and unobstructed view of the animal; its chest was broad and muscular, spanning about five feet, and was sparsely covered in hair. Speaking of the hair, this thing wasn't the typical black, brown or red that most people talk about; it was covered in thick gray hair, and the areas where the hair didn't cover fully, its skin was brown. Its arms were long, thick, like tree trunks, and muscular. This thing looked powerful. I had no doubt that it must have found that dog and simply ripped it in half.

My mind kept telling me to flee, but something in me wanted to look at its face. I know it sounds odd, but I had to, I needed to know what it looked like. Conjuring up the courage, I raised my gaze and for a brief second locked eyes with it but couldn't hold my stare out of fear. What I saw was something familiar yet not. Its face reminded me of a gorilla or ape. It was large, round and brown, and hair didn't cover much of it. Its nose was flat, like a gorilla's, and its teeth, which I was able to see due to its mouth being half open, were not unlike ours. It had big square-like teeth, but I didn't see canines. That didn't mean they weren't there, I just didn't see them, as its mouth was only cracked open in what I can only describe as a sinister sneer. Its eyes were large and black, yet shaped like a human's, but the stare it gave me told me in words not spoken that I wasn't welcome there. I know I presumed what it was thinking, but I have no doubt it was angry with me. Was I in its territory? Did I pose a threat to it? I couldn't see how—I was small and weak compared to it.

On its face, it bore scars, but two were large and distinct. One on its furrowed forehead and the other across its cheek. I wondered years later what could have caused those. Had they come from fights with others, or were they just the remnants of a hard life in the forest?

I fixed my gaze back on its torso. I couldn't help but stare at it. Its gray hair was matted in places, sticks, mud and leaves clung to it, but without any doubt, its hair was fully gray, with patches of silver.

I couldn't fathom how something so large could have walked up without us hearing it. How was it possible that one second it wasn't there, then the next it was standing ten feet from me? My questions were stupid, as it didn't matter; it was there and I needed to make a run for it. I rediscovered my courage, turned and sprinted back the way I'd come. I didn't know if it was coming after me, and I didn't hear anything, but then again, I never heard it approach us. Each step I took I thought could be my last. I had no doubt that if it wanted to get me, it could. My heart raced, lungs burned and legs ached as I tore back up the rocky outcropping, back down the other side and into the area where the others were.

Everyone sat around talking and laughing, their lives seemingly happy with no concerns. My eyes darted around until they settled on my friend, who was sitting on the ground shaking. I could see the terror was still on his face. Standing above him was a counselor, who no doubt also saw his fear and was trying to talk to him.

We didn't discuss the incident until we were both back on the bus heading home. I asked him what he thought about it, and his only response was to shake his head and turn away, which told me he didn't want to discuss it at all.

I've spoken to him years later, and like that day, he still won't talk about it. There's no doubt in my mind that, like me, he still suffers from our brief encounter. I have nightmares, and when I discuss it with anyone, those nightmares increase in frequency. Like many others who've come into contact with these creatures, my experience, those ten seconds, have turned into a lifetime obsession. I have done research on it, gone back into the woods; however, I have my limits, as the more I focus on it, I relapse and become consumed by fear.

I know many like to say the creature is harmless, and I'm sure some are. Like humans, there are some that are benevolent and others that aren't. These are animals and they're also predators. There's not a doubt in my mind that some people have been killed by them, hence all the missing persons cases from national parks and forests over the years.

SHANNON LEGRO & G. MICHAEL HOPF

When I think back to that day, I can still see the one I came up against holding that garment. Whom did that belong to? Had someone else come face-to-face yet wasn't as lucky as me? I'll never know, but I am grateful that I did see it and survived. I know it sounds weird to say that, even though I know I suffer from my experience, I still wouldn't have it any other way.

The one thing I've taken from my encounter is this, these creatures do exist and aren't just in the deep forests of the Pacific Northwest. They also haunt and call home the swaths of land and woods near cities and towns along the eastern seaboard. So the next time you go to a park and think that it'll just be a normal day of hiking, just know that in an instant your perfect bluebird day could turn into a confrontation with a monster who has an appetite for dogs.

THE DEER LEASE

*L*ike I've mentioned before, hunters are a unique group of people who have skills and experience in the woods. They're the ones who have spent a considerable amount of time deep in the forests, so it makes sense that their chances of coming up against or seeing a Bigfoot are greater than those of us who rarely step foot there.

Of the hunters I've talked to who've seen Bigfoot, a good number never go back to hunting for a while, some never. This tells you something. They're armed, trained, yet what they've seen has struck such fear they never can go back again.

This next story details a hunter and how his entire life was impacted by his encounter with not just one, but two Sasquatch.

***

The year was 1979 and I had graduated high school a year before. My family had a deer lease in Northern California, which not only my immediate family used, but my cousins and uncles also hunted on. Everyone primarily went there on the weekends, which meant that the land could be crawling with people, making it much harder to get a deer.

It was getting near the end of deer season, and I hadn't gotten a deer yet, but really wanted to. Knowing that my family, cousins included, would be going up for the weekend, I asked my parents if they'd be fine if I went up midweek.

My parents had no issue with me going, so I packed up and headed out on a Tuesday. I arrived at the gate off the main road around eight at night. Our normal campsite was about a mile in, so I unlocked the heavy gate, passed through and headed to the site. I arrived and promptly unpacked, which included my bike, a motorized dirt bike. I used it to ride farther to where I liked to hunt.

Unpacked, my campsite all set up, and looking forward to a day all alone hunting, I went to sleep.

I woke early, got dressed, and with a pack loaded for a full day, I headed out on my bike, my rifle snug in the scabbard on the side. I rode a mile and a half farther into the woods to a spot I liked to go to. I parked the bike and hiked the rest of the way to my stand, which was nestled alongside a creek.

The day was cool, as you'd expect for an autumn day. I sat in my stand, but nothing came my way all morning. I wanted to take advantage of being out on the lease alone, so I vacated the stand and decided to walk through the woods, with hopes of seeing a deer.

I stayed alongside the creek until I was just down from where my bike was parked along the top of the knoll above me. I turned right and began to hike up, my head swiveling from side to side, looking for a deer or any sign that could tell me they were around.

Suddenly a sense of doom overcame me. It was weird, as I had been feeling fine a second before, but now I felt like something was wrong, like I was in danger. With my senses now heightened, I slowed my pace, but my eyes darted around quickly, expecting to see something. I closed in on the top of the knoll and saw my bike was lying on its side.

From my left a loud bark sounded. It startled me so badly that I literally jumped and at the same time dropped my rifle. I spun my head to the left, and standing thirty-five yards away were two creatures. They were both the same size, standing around five feet tall, covered in short, thick auburn-colored hair, and by the look of them, they weren't happy to see me. Their heads were conical shaped, and their faces were partially covered in hair. They looked like smaller versions of the Patty Sasquatch.

The one on the left barked, and by the

familiar sound of it, I assumed it was the one that barked originally. It stood chest out, hands clenched, and its face was contorted in a way, with its brow furrowed and eyes glaring at me, that it seemed angry with me. It began to growl deeply, gnash its teeth and shake its head. Saliva appeared to pour from its mouth as it growled louder.

I was utterly terrified, my heart thumped hard and my stomach tightened. All I could think was that I was going to die.

The one on the right took a step, reached for a large branch of manzanita shrub, and broke it off with ease. It started to whip it around, hitting everything around it while also jumping up and down in anger.

I got some of my composure back, bent down without looking away from the creatures, and picked up my rifle from the ground. Holding it with a white-knuckled grip, I contemplated putting it to my shoulder, but my fear was too much to overcome. My rifle, a Remington 7mm Magnum, was enough to put them down, but I didn't have the nerve to raise it further. I merely stood, my body trembling uncontrollably. I didn't know what to do. I stared and couldn't get my mind to convince my body to move. I was frozen to the spot.

The two creatures continued to carry on, with the one just staring at me with eyes that could kill and the other whipping the branch around in a frenzy. Minutes ticked by, and soon they began to slowly move on. The one on the left walked down the slope, his eyes glued to me while the other kept thrashing the branch.

Soon they disappeared into some thick brush near the creek. I could still hear them as they whooped and hollered. A short but thick branch came flying towards me and landed feet away. It was their parting gift, you could say.

Finding my courage, I raced up to the top of the knoll, picked up my bike, slipped my rifle into the scabbard on the side, and fired up my bike. While I did all of this, I kept looking around, half expecting them to reappear and attack me.

I turned my bike around and sped off back to the campsite, packed everything up as quickly as I could, and got out of there.

The entire drive back I was overwhelmed with emotion. The intensity of the encounter finally broke me, and I entered my house noticeably upset. My mother asked what was wrong, but I knew there was no way I'd be able to tell them for fear of repercussions.

A week later I found myself back out there, but this time with my family, including my cousins and uncle. I didn't go to the same spot, but it didn't matter. I was terrified and couldn't settle down. Unable to push my fear aside, I got out of the stand and headed back to camp.

That was the last time I went out alone. Now I've gone duck hunting without concern, but there was no way I would ever go back there again, at least not without a large group of people.

Still to this day I've not been able to share my tale for fear of the ridicule and repercussions that would come from it. It's truly sad to think I can't be open and share what happened to me with my family, but I know they'd never understand. I know what I saw, and while I wouldn't mind seeing one again, I'd only want to do so if I could do it without it knowing I was there. The sheer terror of that day has never left me, and to think, I only saw ones that were five feet tall or so; I can't imagine coming face-to-face with one twice as big.

Over the years since, I've done my own armchair research and have come to the conclusion these are purely animals. I know what I saw acted like an animal, but what might sound weird is that it also had a human trait about it. The way that one just stared at me, I've often wondered what it was thinking. Did it want to hurt me? Or was it just trying to scare me? Being that I think these creatures are animals, that probably also makes them territorial, leading me to believe their reaction to me was solely because I was in their woods. I've also wondered why no one else had seen one, and I believe it's because we typically went there on the weekends. Did these things know our schedule and would hightail it out of there? Had I not only intruded on their territory but also during the time they hung out there?

Since that fateful day, I'm filled with many questions and still have a deep-seated fear of ever coming face-to-face with one again because I feel, and this is just an instinct of mine, that while they didn't hurt me, they could have, and I have zero doubt that some do harm people.

While I wouldn't mind seeing one again, I'm also filled with regret that I had the encounter, because before I had no problems, no fear of the woods or what was in it. Now though, I know something that's potentially dangerous and intelligent is there and could pose a threat to me.

My life was altered that day and for the worse.

BIGFOOT IN NEVADA

*I*t is assumed Bigfoot likely roams, or migrates to utilize a better term, to find more accommodating weather, shelter, and abundant protein sources. A state like Nevada (especially the southern half) may not jump to mind as being a viable option for these massive creatures. However, when one is seen in the same month, nearly exactly a year apart, it does beg the question...maybe they do move through an area that would be very surprising to most, on their way to, say...greener pastures.

***

I was raised in Texas, lived in Alaska for some time, and spent a considerable amount of time in the woods hunting. I have a lot of experience with most animals that habitat the forests, but what I saw one night was unlike anything I've ever seen. In fact, I don't know what we saw. The date was December 5, 2005, and my wife and I were heading home after spending time at a friend's house. It was about two thirty in the morning. We were driving down the road, the vast Nevada desert to either side of us, when my headlights suddenly caught sight of something coming at us in our lane.

Initially I thought it was someone on a dirt bike standing up on the foot pegs because it was so tall, moving fast, and it was coming out of the desert with no lights. It started to make a turn to its left, our right, into a housing community that was just off the road. I recall clearly telling my wife that there was no way they would make the turn because of how fast they were going and because I've ridden bikes my whole life. As it began the turn, behind it was a streetlight, which cast its silhouette onto a tall brick wall. It was then I realized it wasn't someone on a dirt bike, but something running on two legs. The best way I can describe it was that it looked like a refrigerator with legs. The chest was so huge, so much so that it looked cartoonish, like it was impossible for something to be this out of proportion in regards to its chest and height.

My wife, who was driving, had a different perspective, and she actually spotted it before I did, standing on the median by a tree. It stepped off the median and began running; this was when I clearly saw it. She immediately accelerated in an attempt to catch up to whatever it was. I know some might think that was crazy, but we were curious. The thing cleared the turn and disappeared. We slowed, made the turn too, but the thing was nowhere in sight. We drove around for a few minutes, but it was gone. I suppose it could have been hiding, but who knows. Filled with confusion about what we'd just seen, we headed home, which wasn't far.

The next day this terrible putrid smell was around our house. It was so bad my wife complained that it burned her eyes. This smell remained around our house for three days.

I eventually drove back to the spot where we'd had our sighting, and looked around. While there, I measured the wall. With the creature towering a head above it, I now knew it stood over seven feet tall.

I later called my friend and, without hesitation, told him what had happened. I thought that he'd think I was crazy, but that wasn't the case. He proceeded to tell me a story of his own that had taken place years before.

He and a group of friends were out in the area. It was night and they had a campfire going. A woman who was with them suddenly began to scream in terror. They all looked at what she was pointing at and saw this thing towering over his truck, looking down on them. He said it was huge and covered in fur that resembled the color of a coyote. One of the men in the group jumped up and gave chase, but the thing sped up a foothill with amazing speed. When it crested the top of the hill, it stopped, looked back and yelled at them before disappearing.

Two weeks went by and five of the nine people that were with him that night were in town. I went to my friend's house and brought up his story to those there. One person quickly got up and left the room. The other four promptly acknowledged that the story was true without question. What's interesting is his encounter also happened in December; this has led me to theorize that these things migrate through the area at that time.

Since then we've not seen anything near our house or where we saw the creature before, but that pungent odor has returned now and then. Most recently when it came back, it lasted for two to three days and then disappeared. Also over the years my wife has said that our dogs seem to sense something lurking around the property. They bark and act aggressive, yet we've not seen nor found any evidence.

What we experienced that night was a brief encounter with a Bigfoot, that I have no doubt of. The naysayers all cast dispersions, but we can't unsee what we saw. There's no doubt in my mind that these creatures exist, and I fear the only way they'll be proven is for a body to be brought in; this means one will have to be killed. However, until that day, I'll always cast a cautious glance down the darkly lit highway at night or be on alert when I step outside my house. I don't know if I'll ever see one again, but if given a chance to, I'd take it.

BIG RED EYE

*E*ncountering a Bigfoot is a rare event. I've sought them out, yet I've never had the opportunity and privilege to lay eyes on the creature. However, there are those who have, which makes those cases as uncommon as winning the lottery...twice. The next story details such an occurrence. You read his first encounter in Chapter 5. While his first face-to-face was by pure chance, it sparked in him an obsession to discover all he could about Bigfoot. His research led to his second encounter, one that you'll find was as equally disturbing as his first, and one that would mark the official end of his quest.

***

It's not often someone has one encounter with Bigfoot, but two has got to be something very special or just bad luck. I'm going for bad luck here even though this time I went seeking the creatures. In Chapter 5 I detailed the first time I came up against the monster. I was thirteen then and it altered my life forever. Years after I have suffered from what must be PTSD. I've had nightmares and a fear that sometimes makes it impossible to even go near the woods. However, I also came away from that moment obsessed and wanting to know more. I know it sounds odd to have PTSD yet go looking for the one thing that gave me my PTSD. I don't know how to describe it, but I'm conflicted. I never wanted to see the creature again, yet I did; again, I know that sounds weird.

Flash forward years after my first encounter, and I was actively conducting research near where I live in northern New Jersey. I was online looking up sightings, talking to people, and even interviewing locals. A friend of mine, Hugh, had joined me in this endeavor, and after collecting a bunch of data and information, we picked a site to do extensive fieldwork.

This place is in the Wyanokie Highlands in northern New Jersey. The Highlands stretch from eastern Pennsylvania, across upper New Jersey and into southern New York State. The site we go to is a rarely used campsite but is close to reported sightings of *Old Red Eye,* which is an old Native American name for Bigfoot in the area. The campsite is adjacent to the land of a man I met on a hike. He told me old folk stories about Red Eye and even detailed his own odd encounters.

One really stuck with me; he told me that he'd get banging on the side of his house. He'd look outside but see nothing. What he told me next has always sent shivers down my spine. He said that he got the feeling they were attempting to lure him outside. I heard that and asked myself the question, for what? Why would they do that? I know the creatures are big and powerful and could bust down any door, so why lure someone outside? It's all so strange and creepy.

Armed with a place to go, we arrived at the campsite and got to work. We cut a trail using hatchets about a mile long deep into the woods and adjacent to the reported sightings but in an area that is not frequented by humans. I'm not an expert by no means, but this just seemed like the right plan of attack. I thought it important to go to an area where these creatures might live, and I figured it had to be somewhere no human went.

For two months we regularly went, hiked the trail, but never heard nor saw anything. Then one day while back in the woods, we discovered a game trail, and imprinted clearly in the moist earth were a set of footprints, one large and one small. When I say large, I mean *big*, like tracks left by a Bigfoot. Hugh looked at me in disbelief and asked, "Are these real?"

I could feel the fear coming back as I suddenly thought that it all could happen again. I saw the massive monster with the dog ripped in half clutched in its grip, it looking down on me with its angry scowl. Unable to control the fear, I turned and ran. He was able to stop me and convince me that we had to stay and investigate. He implored my sense of reason based upon the fact that we'd just spent the last two months out here.

Feeling calm yet concerned, we went back to the tracks and followed them; however, after a short distance they just disappeared. Unable to continue the search, we went back home. Our two months of effort had paid off though, as we'd discovered tracks: one of an adult Bigfoot and one of a juvenile. I now had proof that they were there and close by.

Two weeks went by, not for any logistical reason, but because it took me that long to muster the courage to go. It took me two weeks to muster the courage to go back out.

We arrived at the campsite and headed out to the area where we'd found the tracks. We got there, and to our shock, we found a dead bear. What made this grisly discovery horrifying was that the bear, lying on its belly, had its head twisted one hundred and eighty degrees and looking up at the sky.

Both of us became immediately creeped out, but I was determined not to allow this to get the better of me. Hugh pulled out a camera and snapped photographs. As I stood over the body, I looked at Hugh and said, "This is the place."

We found a place to camp for the night and set up, which wasn't much, as we'd only brought sleeping bags, water and food. We chatted, smoked cigarettes, and prepared for whatever might happen. When the sun set, I decided I'd do some wood knocks with a thick branch I'd found earlier. With each knock, I'd wait patiently for a reply, but nothing, no reply, no distinct knock from farther off in the woods. I noticed that everything around us had gotten quiet, no crickets, and no sounds that you'd associate with being in the woods. I could hear the crickets off in the distance, but nothing in our immediate area. However, we weren't alone, as what can only be described as a loud roar came from the top of the ridge to my left.

On the heels of that, just a few seconds after, a bloodcurdling scream came from the top of the ridge to my right.

Terrified, Hugh too screamed, jumped up and looked around.

I shot him a look and said, "Please sit down, please; and whatever you do, don't run." All I could imagine now was him taking off, not only leaving me there alone, but worse, he'd become the prey, and I feared they'd chase him down.

What was so odd was we both hadn't heard anything move before this. No movement through the woods, no branches breaking, no leaves rustling, nothing. I wasn't sure what to think. Had they been there the entire time? Or were they truly this stealthy? I instantly recalled my first encounter and how it had just appeared in front of me, again, without making a sound.

Hugh sat back down. We exchanged a few

encouraging words by telling each other that everything was going to be okay, but deep down inside I was terrified and wondered if we'd survive the night.

Another roar erupted from the ridgeline to the left, with a scream to our right coming on its heels, and as soon as the scream ended, the roar sounded again. This went on for about ten or so seconds then abruptly ended, giving us a reprieve of silence. We both glanced at each other. I could see Hugh's eyes were as wide as saucers, and I imagined mine were too. I prayed, hoping that was it, but my prayers weren't answered, as crashing came from both sides.

They were now coming towards us. My body tensed as I felt that soon they'd be on top of us, and then I imagined being ripped apart. I could see heavy brush to either side of me and just waited for them to emerge. I could feel my heart beating hard and fast. I kept my eyes glued on the brush, just waiting to see it come barreling out, but they both stopped just on the other side, just out of sight.

I craned my head to the right and saw a silhouette for a brief second; then it moved back into the brush. I didn't know what was going on. Were they taunting us? Was this a game to them, or were they just trying to scare us?

Frozen in fear, we sat and stared at the brush. We knew they were there, but they didn't make a sound. It was quiet save our own shaking and mumbling. The seconds turned to minutes then hours with nothing else occurring. The sun eventually rose, and to our surprise there was nothing in the brush. With the light of the sun, we grabbed our things and hiked out of the area, our heads swiveling around with anticipation of seeing one of the creatures. We made it back to the campsite with no issue, loaded up the car and drove out.

As we drove, I asked him what he thought about our encounter. He confessed that he thought the tracks we'd found were probably made by people and even questioned if the sounds and movement were also made by people. I challenged that premise because I knew that no human could have made that roar or scream, and that the crashing in the woods clearly came from something huge.

I asked if he'd seen the silhouette, but he hadn't because out of fear, he'd kept his head down. We didn't talk much more about it, and I got the sense he was in denial. He really kept wanting to think it was just someone out there either playing a prank or messing with us. I know how hard it can be for people to accept that these creatures are real, and I can only say with conviction that they are.

I haven't gone back into the woods since by myself or with only one other person. I'm just too afraid that if I have another encounter, the next one might be my last. I've continued to follow sightings and even tried to talk to the land owner whose land is adjacent to the campsite, but haven't been able to reach him. I'm not afraid to tell anyone what I've experienced, and I don't care what the naysayers or skeptics say because I know without a doubt what I've seen and what I've heard. I tried to get Hugh to talk about it, but he won't. Maybe one day he'll open up about it, but until then I just leave him alone.

Since my first encounter and past my second, I've sought counseling and still today have nightmares. These nightmares have me curled up in the corner, sometimes in my house, other times in the woods, and I know the creature is close by. I can hear it coming, moving towards me with speed and purpose. I'm too afraid to look up, so I keep my eyes pressed closed, the heavy footfalls thumping loudly, and just before it reaches me, I wake.

I've had this nightmare over and over again, all the same, but the place is different. I don't know if I'll ever not feel the emotional and psychological effects from my two encounters; in fact, I'm willing to wager that I won't.

I don't know what Bigfoot is or how it's

been able to escape capture over so many years. I can only guess that it's highly intelligent and has keen senses. So often I put human traits on the animal, but I don't know how else to explain its behavior. I do hope that one day concrete evidence is found and presented to the world. I really want people to see that such a thing exists and that it's closer to them than they might guess.

For those who live close to cities or suburban areas on the east coast, know this, Bigfoot is real and is probably lurking in some pocket of woods or forests near you. It's not just in the Pacific Northwest but could be just inside the tree line in your backyard, watching you right now.

DIRE WOLF UNDER A SUPERMOON

I have what I refer to as the 'No List.' It covers many different phenomena and possible situations. These range anywhere from waking to a shadow person standing over your bed, to a small manlike creature in overalls perched on a log nearby, reading a book you had next to your sleeping bag while on a solo camping trip. (Thanks for this nightmare, John Olsen!) But one creature whose sighting always elicits fear and thoughts of death is that of a Dogman. (BTW, I do loathe this term, I can't pronounce Wolfman properly, and werewolf denotes a man that changes into the creature, so I guess Dogman has to be it.) The Dogman seems to almost always be in a foul mood and doesn't really care if you see him. This is quite

117

unfortunate for many witnesses, because these things are horrifying amalgamations of muscle, tissue, and bone. Attach a snout full of teeth, and we're off to the nightmare races. First place? The ultimate prize of never sleeping again.

***

A few years back I got the bad news that my mother had been diagnosed with lung cancer. Not hesitating, I packed my things and moved to a rural area east of Oklahoma City to help my brother and his wife care for my mother. I'm a registered nurse and figured my expertise could be helpful. I managed to get a job on a nightshift at a facility about forty minutes away. This enabled me to take my mom to her doctor appointments and chemotherapy during the day.

My brother's house sat on about three acres, with the closest neighbor nowhere in sight. The area itself was wooded and sparsely populated.

Before I had my encounter, I had two other experiences that occurred, which I believe might be connected.

The first experience happened one night around nine thirty when I was heading to work. I was driving towards town on old Highway 66. There was nothing around but trees and an old abandoned gas station that is not designated as a historical landmark. I was focused on the road when suddenly deer came racing across the highway in front of me. As a note, when I say highway, it's really just a two-lane road.

The way the deer acted, it appeared they were running away or fleeing something that was chasing them. I slammed on the brakes to avoid hitting them and came to a full stop. My knuckles were wrapped in a white-knuckle grip on the steering wheel, and my heart was thumping from nearly missing the deer. To my right sat the abandoned gas station, no other cars on the road. Just as I was about to take off, I heard a growl. I didn't know what to think. I looked and it seemed to be coming from the gas station. Fear rose in me. Not sure what I was hearing, but not wanting to stay around any longer, I sped off. I got to work safely, but I was a bit shaken. I finally brushed it off and thought it was probably a local animal. Coming from Colorado, we have big cats, so maybe they have something similar in Oklahoma and the cat was chasing the deer.

Days later I was driving down the same stretch of road at night when to my left, I saw a pair of red glowing eyes. What was odd was they were very high off the ground. I was thinking to myself what it could be and instantly thought of the growl I'd heard. I drove home without incident but felt the need to go back to investigate during the day to see if there was something there that might have been reflecting the light, but didn't find anything.

Some time passed and I was at my brother's house. I had just gotten a new camera, and I hadn't quite mastered it. I went to the front yard, which was about an acre in size with a six-foot fence around the perimeter. Something to note, the front door of his house is always locked; they never use it, as people come and go by using the kitchen door.

I was in the front yard with my dog. There was a supermoon that night, so I was excited about what photographs I could get with my new camera. As I was snapping photos of the moon, I got a bad feeling. It was enough that I decided to take my dog back inside. I immediately went back out front and shot a few more shots.

Eager to see some of the shots I'd taken, I went back and sat on the front porch. As I was scrolling through the pictures, I caught something out of the corner of my eye. I looked up and to my shock I saw a huge doglike creature. It was on all fours, sniffing the ground. It was walking so that I only saw its profile, and it ended up about fifteen feet in front of me. I can't tell you how terrified I was.

Here I was, the glow of my camera display screen shining on me, and there in front of me was this huge creature covered in matted gray hair. It turned its head away from me and towards the moon, which was low on the horizon.

The creature on all fours was over four feet tall, and it stretched from snout to tail about six feet. Its hind legs were huge, and its front legs or arms were covered in thick hair. The back was hunched, it reminded me of a hyena, but around its neck, it resembled a lion's mane, as the hair there was thick. When it turned its head forward again, I could see the long snout and pointed ears. What was so shocking was how quietly this large creature moved. It almost glided in a way. It took a moment, but soon the odor of wet dog washed over me.

Sitting there, frozen in fear, I had no place to go. I had a camera in my hands yet no power or courage to raise it. If I had, the flash would have gone off and exposed me. Fearing for my life, I kept perfectly still. I wanted to run, I wanted to scream, but I just knew that if I did anything, I'd be risking my life.

The creature lowered its head and again began sniffing the ground. It made some unusual sounds, like grunting and movements that made it seem unnatural. It moved forward stealthily until it disappeared around the side of the house. I wanted to go inside, but the door behind me was locked, and the kitchen door was in the same direction the creature had gone. With no exit strategy, I went and hid behind a bench on the porch and prayed the creature wouldn't return.

As I sat trembling from my encounter, I began to wonder what it was I'd just seen. Was it a dog? If it was, it was the largest and most powerful I'd ever seen in my life. The only word that popped in my head was *werewolf* because that was exactly what it looked like. I questioned how it didn't know I was there. It didn't make sense that it hadn't seen me, much less smelled me; I know that dogs have a good sense of smell. Was it stalking something else? There were so many questions and no answers.

Twenty minutes or so went by, and I found the courage to head back inside. I carefully rounded the corner but saw nothing. Back inside, I locked the house down and went to bed, although I didn't sleep well. The next day I mentioned what I'd seen to my brother. He didn't laugh it off; he simply said that there were big dogs around the area.

I told him that this wasn't a big dog per se, but something huge, massive in size, much larger than any dog I'd ever seen. I went to work later on and told some co-workers; their response was typical of most, as they laughed and said I was crazy.

I spent the next year at my brother's house, living in fear of encountering the creature again, but thankfully never saw it. Since then I've become obsessed with figuring out what I saw. Knowing that I'm not alone, as others have seen something similar, I feel vindicated that I'm not crazy or that I hadn't mistaken what I saw. I've been asked if I'm grateful for my sighting, and I'd say I'm not, although I would see one again, but only if I were in safe place, like in a tank.

LEGEND BECAME REALITY

I *have asked many interviewees what their perfect sighting would be. How close would it be, how much of it would you want to see...would it see you? As a researcher, I believe we've all wondered if we ever struck Sasquatch gold...how it would play out. In Ohio, an oft-mentioned mecca for Bigfoot, Ray Gardner had been looking into Sasquatch for quite some time. He approaches the study with a scientific eye and formulates theories on their etiology, possible movements through the state, what a family unit might look like, etc. When he finally saw one standing behind a friend in an open field...it abruptly brought the legend of Sasquatch for him into a reality.*

***

I have been researching Sasquatch for many years. I've found a plethora of evidence—from footprints, tree breaks and recordings of vocalizations—but hadn't yet had a sighting until one fateful night.

I was out with friends and fellow Sasquatch researchers Tim and Jeremy. We had certain areas we often visited, with this one being a hotbed for activity. We'd been out all day and were about to wrap it up for the night. It was about ten thirty at night roughly, and we were driving out. I asked Tim to pull over to see if we could see any deer. He had a big Ford F-150 with KC lights mounted on it. We stopped and looked around for a while but saw nothing. He finally turned the truck off and killed the lights. I stepped out with a 4-D Maglite in hand, turned it on, and scanned the area we couldn't see with the truck lights. I crossed over a field with tall weeds and saw a set of neon green eyes glowing. I asked Tim to look at what I was seeing.

Tim and Jeremy both came over and saw what I saw, a set of eyes moving from left to right just above the top of the weeds. Now I judged that the weeds stood about four feet tall, so I thought this thing had to have some size. I could see the eyes moving, but when it appeared to look straight at us, the eyes appeared to be every bit of ten inches apart, making whatever it was pretty large.

I'll be honest, my first thought was this was probably a horse, because I couldn't quite make out what it was, just the eye shine. We stood watching it go from left to right until it disappeared into the woods. The entire time I was thinking to myself that this thing was really big.

We talked for a bit before a light misty rain settled in on us. We decided to hop back in the truck and go get a cup of coffee. Just as we pulled out to drive off, Jeremy said that he wanted to go confirm the height of the weeds, as he didn't believe they were as tall as I said they were.

We all agreed and pulled the truck into a place where we now could use the KC lights to assist us. Jeremy got out and headed over to the area. As he was moving through the weeds, we were hollering at him to go either left or right, to better help guide him to the exact spot.

When Jeremy hit the weeds, I now saw that I was wrong, the weeds were bigger than I thought, making whatever we saw that much larger. Jeremy stands six feet, and the top of the weeds were at his shoulders. As he was moving along, he kept looking back to the truck but couldn't see due to the KC lights blinding him. I was navigating him by giving him directions, and he was moving along nicely.

When he got to within forty yards of where we'd seen the eyes, they appeared again right out of the brush. The eyes were staring right at Tim and me. Alarmed, I hollered out to Jeremy that the eyes were back.

Again, I still thought this was probably a horse. Jeremy asked where the eyes were, and I told him they were to his right. He promptly turned and headed that way.

He was about thirty yards away when shockingly this thing stood straight up and now towered over everything around it, including Jeremy, making him look like a ten-year-old. The glowing eyes were now looking down on Jeremy from underneath the overhang of a tree.

My first thought when I saw that this wasn't a horse was that Jeremy was dead. There was no way we'd be able to get to him in time. Now my mind tried to rationalize that this thing was probably a bear on its hind legs. All I kept saying to myself was, "That is one big bear."

I hollered out for Jeremy to freeze. Jeremy did as I ordered. After years researching together, he knew I don't panic, but he could hear it now in my voice. I then shouted that he needed to come back...now!

Jeremy didn't hesitate; he began to walk backwards towards the truck. From his vantage point and because the lights of the truck were so bright, he still couldn't see what we were seeing.

After Jeremy retreated fifteen yards, Tim and I finally got a good clear look at what it was.

It swung its shoulder around and pivoted to go back into the woods. The KC lights caught it just right, allowing us to see its back, arms, buttocks and legs. With its full back facing us, I could now see how wide its shoulders were, and I swear it was every bit of four feet wide. It was covered in blackish brown hair that was thick. It took a step and disappeared into the heavy canopy of the woods. It then dawned on me that this wasn't a bear either.

I think back on that night and now believe the first time we saw the eyes, it was on all fours crossing the field. We reported our sighting and others came out to find evidence.

They measured the overhang where it finally stood up, and came back that it was over eight feet. This makes sense, as Jeremy appeared like a small child in comparison to it.

After all the times I've spent in the woods, the countless hours, the cold nights and hot summer days, I'd finally seen one. What had been legend was now reality, and I'd never be the same.

SHANNON LEGRO & G. MICHAEL HOPF

FAR TOO CLOSE

I occasionally get correspondence from listeners who, after hearing an experience shared on iTF, have a memory of their own surface. Some of these are truly terrifying memories that may have been better left buried. A summer sleepover is supposed to be filled with too much candy, movies so bad they're good, and little sleep...with a scary bedtime story thrown in every now and then for good measure. What you don't expect is for a real-life monster to be just through two thin panes of glass.

***

The story I'm about to tell you happened many years ago at my cousins' house near Danbury, Wisconsin, in the northwestern part of the state. What's so odd is I've only recently recalled what happened. All I can say is that I had blocked it out of my memory; then one night as I was working night shift, I had a creepy and uncomfortable feeling spread across my body. Something began to rise, my stomach tightened, and before I knew it, I was filled with terror. Then it came to me, I could see my cousins' house, and right on the heels of that, the word *werewolf* popped into my mind. I don't know why I suddenly began to remember that night, but I can guess why I'd forgotten it. What I saw that night shook me to the core and terrified me.

I was about seven years old and was at my cousins' house for the summer. I went up there a lot growing up because they lived on a lake. This gave us a lot to do during the hot and long summer days.

Their house was a single-level home, and the bedroom I stayed in was at the end of the house, with the other bedrooms located on the opposite side. The house itself was in a sparsely populated area. There were neighbors close by, but none that you could see if you were outside. So when you were out there, it felt like you were all alone.

It was late at night; I'm guessing it was about eleven thirty. My cousin, who was about my age, and I had been sent to bed an hour earlier. Of course, being kids, we stayed up joking around and talking. His bed was on the right wall, mine on the left; in between us was a large window. We had the lights off, but a half-moon combined with a light that was affixed to a pole out front lit the room enough for us to see both inside and outside. We usually kept the window cracked during the summers to let in the cool summer air. Tonight wasn't any different. Like every other night, the calming sound of crickets and other critters could be heard.

We were laughing about something when my cousin suddenly stopped and asked if I heard something.

At first I didn't hear anything. I kept listening intently; then what sounded like long nails scratching the wood siding of the house hit my ears. I faced him and ask if that was the sound he'd heard. He confirmed it was.

Instantly we were both freaking out. We didn't know what it could be, but there wasn't any doubt something was just outside our window. After a short time period, I noticed the crickets and frogs had stopped. I asked my cousin if he'd noticed, and he said he had. This only added to our fear. Not a few seconds went by before we heard a throaty growl; it wasn't too loud but enough for us to hear. As you look at the window, the growl had come from the right side of it.

The growl grew closer until we could see something just at the right edge of the window. We couldn't tell what it was, but something was there. It began to appear now from the right edge until we saw what looked like the side of a dog's head; its snout stuck out about six to seven inches, and on top of its head were pointed ears. It really reminded me of a wolf or German shepherd, but it was impossible for this to be that, as where it was in the window made it much taller, and it also appeared to be standing.

We both stared, unsure what we were looking at. It moved from right to left and stopped in the center of the window. There was where it rose until it was more upright. I could make out its massive shoulders, which sloped down to its hunched back. With my eyes wide with fear, I watched as it sniffed the air, the growl we'd heard initially still coming from its clenched jaw. It never looked at us nor did it move its head, something I'm thankful for, as I don't know what I would've done if it looked at me or even acknowledged I was there. It then rose even taller until we couldn't see its head. As we stared out the window, we saw thick, muscular arms and hands. Now towering where it was, I have to guess it stood about seven feet tall. Like I said, its arms were thick, muscular and covered in a short grayish-colored hair, almost resembling the color of a wolf or coyote. I could make out its skin color too, which looked dark, almost black in color. It proceeded to move towards the left, its snout constantly sniffing, until it walked past the window completely and disappeared out of sight.

Freaked out, we sat silent, our eyes fixed on the window. I can't recall how long we just sat there, but it was minutes. Finally, my cousin jumped up and slammed the window shut. He climbed back in bed, turned to me, and asked if I knew what it was we'd just seen.

The only word that could come to mind at the time was *werewolf*. I could see he was scared. He followed up by saying that we should go to bed. He lay down, his back towards me. I did the same thing, my mind spinning with what we'd just seen. I can't recall how long I lay there, but eventually fell asleep.

We woke and immediately told his younger sister that we'd seen a werewolf. She didn't believe us. We then told his older brother, he was about eighteen; he didn't quite blow it off, but he also didn't act like he believed us either. So there we were with no one ready to accept what we'd seen.

I stayed a couple more days, my cousin and I discussed it, but that was about it. I returned over the Christmas break, but again didn't discuss it. As the months bled into years, I forgot about the terrifying sighting, relegating it to the dark corners of my mind, only to recently have it come back. I did see my cousin over those years very infrequently but never discussed it. I've since lost contact with him and have tried to find his contact information now that the memory has come roaring back into my life, but have been unable to.

With my memory now intact, I've spent time online researching Dogmen and if there have been other sightings or encounters in that area. I've come to find there have been. I listen to programs, including *iNTO THE FRAY*, for stories, not just because I'm now curious but to learn more about what I saw that night.

As I sit here writing this, I can say I don't feel lucky to have seen it. I've heard other people's stories, and they say they're grateful for the encounter, not me, the only thing I'm grateful for is that it didn't look at me. Like I said, I think I would have died from fright had it peered through those two thin panes of glass at me. I don't know what it was doing or where it was going, but my cousin and I saw something that is unexplainable. I now wonder how many times this thing had come up to the house. Had it been lurking around all along and we only happened to see it out of pure luck, or did we do something to cause it to come up? I'll never know the answer. I feel a kinship to others who have seen or witnessed this type of creature. I know I never want to see it again, but my curiosity is engaged and I'll keep researching so I can understand what we saw that night so many years ago.

I want to finish by saying I'm thankful for

Shannon and *iNTO THE FRAY*. We've become friends, and it was because of her show that I do have some peace with what occurred that night. It still scares me to think about it, but being able to share has allowed me to let go of that fear, which I've had all of these years. Thank you, Shannon.

IN THESE WOODS

William Jevning coined the phrase "Underwear-Changing Moment." It's self-explanatory and the perfect synopsis of a situation that can quickly become unfavorable for a person who is much smaller and inferior in the woods compared to the creature known as Bigfoot. For Michael and his cousins…a simple walk in the woods behind his grandparents' home in Ohio turns into a scary lesson in the maternal instincts of a massive female Sasquatch. As you will find out, this wasn't the last of his experiences.

***

My family was visiting my grandparents' house in southern Ohio many years ago. It was a great property that I enjoyed going to, as we could be outside. This was helped by their land backing up to Wayne National Forest, giving us a vast area to play in. My cousin, who lived across from them, had land too. On my cousin's side of the hill, as we used to call it, there were natural springs and fruit trees located deep in the woods, something we liked to visit when we were there.

The particular day in question was a nice fall day, I can't recall if it was September or October, but it was definitely fall. I headed out to the woods with my cousin, who was seventeen, and my older sister. As we headed up a game trail that coursed along the side of the mountain, we heard some noise about halfway up. We didn't think much about it because we often saw deer and other game when we were out in the woods. I was ahead of everyone and reached the top of the ledge first. A small and shallow stream-fed pond sat atop the mountain, and alongside it were fruit trees. On the opposite side, about forty yards away, I spotted movement. I looked and saw what at first looked like a little monkey, about three and a half feet tall with black hair, playing in the water. It ran from the water and playfully began to climb a fruit tree. I wasn't really alarmed, as I was more curious, and moved closer to get a better look.

At this time, my sister and cousin reached the top, saw the creature and froze. I kept moving, as I really wanted to see this thing closer. I moved another fifteen or so feet and got a better look at it. All I can say from my experience then is it looked like an orangutan, that's the best way to describe it. It was then the thing saw me. It stopped what it was doing, let out a shriek, turned on a dime, and raced off into a grouping of pine trees. Seconds later, two tall southern yellow pines started shaking. I turned back and went to where my sister and cousin were; they hadn't moved an inch since spotting the creature. I asked them what they thought was going on, with my cousin responding in urgency that we needed to get out of there immediately. I didn't understand, for me, an eleven-year-old, I just thought this was just a small monkey and didn't think anything else beyond that.

My cousin told me that lately something in the area had been causing a disturbance. Deer and other animals had been getting killed; the bodies they found had their necks snapped and parts of their bodies ripped off.

It was then that the trees started to shake even more violently. We turned and watched as a large cinnamon-colored creature emerged from the group of trees, with the smaller monkey on its shoulder. The larger creature was massive, and I could easily tell it was a female because I could see its breasts. The thing's face was more humanlike than the smaller one.

At that moment we had two choices: stay and keep staring, or turn and get the hell out of there. The quickest way to get to the road that led to my grandparents' house was to head back down the slope, which was angled at forty-five degrees. Not hesitating, we began

BEYOND THE FRAY: BIGFOOT

our quick descent, mainly by sliding down on our butts; this happened just as the creature began to come for us. As I was heading down, not gracefully I should add, I looked back and saw this thing standing at the top of the ledge. It looked down at us, and with incredible ease, it shoved a boulder-sized piece of shale down the slope towards us.

Fortunately we reached the bottom, saw the shale barreling down, got out of the way, and watched it crash into a ditch alongside the road. If we hadn't been able to see it coming and moved, the massive piece of shale would have hit us. We ran across the road, crossed a creek, and got to my grandparents' house.

We didn't say a word to them though they could tell something had happened, as we all looked white as a ghost. That trip we never encountered anything else.

After we left, my grandmother did ask my cousin about why we looked so freaked, and he told her the story. She didn't think it foolish or discount our tale.

As the years went on, I heard stories about the property and creatures similar to what we saw lurking around. I would eventually see photographs taken from trail cameras. In them it showed the female, which we saw, and the juvenile, but it also showed the male. The father's appearance closely resembled that of a gorilla.

As I got older, so many things became clear to me, specifically all the warnings my grandparents would express to us when we were there. For instance, they always told us to walk not run while we were in the woods. I can only assume that's because 'prey' runs, and if we ran, we'd be sport for those creatures, and they also told us if we heard something barreling through the woods, get out of its way because it was something you didn't want to encounter.

One story that gives me chills is the one my grandmother told me. One late night my grandfather left to go to town, a far and long trip back then. While he was gone, something came to the house, got on the roof, and was making a ton of racket. My grandmother and the nine kids she had, one included my mother, all were there and attest to this account. They said that from late evening until near dawn something was jumping up and down on the roof. They were terrified by the incident. The second my grandfather came home, the thing fled. No one ever saw what it was, but the way my grandmother describes it, it sounds as if it was huge and caused a lot of damage.

There are other stories, but too many to mention, about these creatures and my grandparents' land. Looking back on my encounter, I can say that it's made me very cautious when I enter the woods, especially an area I'm not familiar with. I can't say that I'm scared, I'm just not careless. Since then I've seen the creature other times, but farther away than that day over twenty-six years ago, when I was eleven years old. When I've been asked what I think the creature is, I reply that I believe it's a flesh and blood animal. I also believe the species is abundant and thrives from coast to coast in North America. I can't explain why we've never been able to capture one or find a dead body, but they're out there. Maybe we don't find a body because they're good at burying their own dead, and the reason we can't capture one alive is because they're just too good at being elusive. There's no doubt in my mind the government is aware of them, especially the park and forest service. I've talked to some who work in those agencies, and they hint about areas to stay away from without giving full disclosure of what or why I should avoid certain areas.

When it comes to why the government wants to hide their existence, it has to come down to we as a society wouldn't be able to handle the truth. It would also hurt commercial interests and also lead to groups wanting to shut down logging or mining operations on public land.

Whatever the reasons for our collective

inability to prove their existence, I know what I saw that day and the other times. These creatures are out there and are territorial in nature as well as protective like we humans are for their young. Here's some advice if you ever see a juvenile, get as far away from it as you can because its mother is probably not too far away and will most definitely not be happy with you.

BIGFOOT OF THE GREAT WHITE NORTH

*R*oad sightings make up many of the Bigfoot reports out there. I've mentioned that a confirmed sighting of a Sasquatch while driving may be quite the ideal way to view one. You are behind a decent amount of metal that is capable of forward motion in the event things get hairy, pun intended. As if one of these experiences isn't enough, an even closer encounter may have you asking if a move to a big city—sans trees, solitude, fresh air, and massive hairy bipeds—may be advantageous.

***

I've had two encounters with Sasquatch, and my most recent one from 2015 scared the shit out of me. I've been reluctant to tell my stories, but I do because I feel I must. Let me clear that I don't go on any Bigfoot groups or watch anything online because most of it is bullshit and a waste of my time. To be honest, I don't think the idea of the creature is that exciting; it's just life. They exist and that's all I can say on that.

Let me start with my first encounter. I was fourteen and living in the remote community of Cross Lake, in central Manitoba. I was going to a residential school there and got to meet a lot of people, many natives, and became close friends with some. During winter break, a friend and I decided to go snowmobiling. Well, we were driving down the hydro line when suddenly I noticed fresh tracks in the snow. What made them peculiar was they looked like footprints. They were right along the trail and appeared to come out of the bush then turn and go back in, as if something came out and we scared it, so it went back into the bush. Curious, I stopped.

My friend, who is from the area, stopped too and asked what I was doing and urged me to continue. I brushed him off. I hopped off my sled to get a better look at the tracks.

The tracks were about two feet deep, fourteen inches long and five feet separated each track. They were in a circular pattern, and you could see where they came from the bush onto the side of the trail, turned and went back into the bush. My friend became adamant about leaving, but I was having too much fun. I then smelled something horrible. Never in my life had I smelled anything like this, nor have I since, and the best way to describe it is to say it was as close to a unique smell as a dead body. I'm not saying it smelled like a dead body, but it was as unique as that is and as horribly gross to the senses.

The instant my friend got a whiff, he turned on his sled and took off without waiting for me or saying another word. I was shocked by his behavior, but still hadn't gotten the clue yet that staying around wasn't so smart. I was being me, a curious fourteen-year-old. I couldn't stop being fascinated by the tracks and now the smell. My starry-eyed wonder quickly vanished when something massive with black hair stood up, its back facing me.

From my vantage point all I could see was from the waist up. I couldn't get an estimate of the height at the time, but after having seen moose; this thing towered over them. Its shoulders were wide, and the hair on its back got longer the higher you went. With my curiosity now replaced by fear, I jumped on my sled, fired it up and sped off.

To this day, I can't confirm it was a Sasquatch, as I didn't see its face, but I believe it was because of the size of it, the fact it was on two legs,the unique smell and the area is well known for sightings. My friend at the time still won't talk about it, but his actions told me then and still tell me that he was aware of the creature in the area. When I caught up with him later, I peppered him with questions. All he did was respond by saying for us not to mention it or tell anyone about it. I'm not sure if he'd ever seen one, but his strong desire not to stop, then the way he acted after smelling the odor and his subsequent conduct told me everything I needed to know. I'm guessing now that something happened to my friend.

I'll say this, my first encounter scared me, but it didn't change my life. I think if I didn't have my second encounter, I would barely remember the first incident and probably joke about it or say I saw something but without passion or conviction. What happened on July 3, 2015, at 3:47 p.m. changed my life; it shattered my paradigm completely and utterly.

***

I was in need of a vacation. I was dealing with some stress and just needed to get out of town. I had some vacation days, so I put in for a week off and got it. My plan was to go to northern Manitoba and visit relatives. At this time I was living in Winnipeg, so it would be quite a drive. Along the way I wanted to check out Cedar Lake. It's a huge beautiful lake, and I really wanted to find a way in so I could come back with my son and girlfriend for a nice camping trip.

I came across a possible access to the lake and wanted to see if it worked. Luck was on my side, as I found the road, if you want to call it that. It was a narrow pothole-riddled dirt road and not easily passable because I couldn't go faster than five miles per hour for fear I'd wreck my car. I made a turn, and through a cut in the trees, I could see the lake ahead. I was getting excited 'cause I was almost there, I was guessing about a quarter mile away now.

I then caught a glimpse of something ahead of me, about a hundred yards away, walking towards me on the right-hand side of the road. I leaned in and looked closer. This thing had its head down, and it was just shuffling down the side of the road. My first instinct was that it was a person, but as I drew closer, I began to get this thought that it might not be a person after all. My heart started racing and my thoughts began to shift to the idea that this could be a Sasquatch.

I slowed my car to a stop and stared at this thing. It was coming closer and closer; then it stopped, lifted its head, stiffened its stature and stared at me for what seemed like an eternity. It then jolted into the bush and disappeared. All I wanted to do was turn around, but I couldn't, the road was too narrow. The only way for me to go was forward.

My heart was beating a million times a second and I was breathing hard. I couldn't just sit there; I had to go down to the lake so I could turn around. As I contemplated my next move, I also debated what I'd just seen. Over and over I told myself I hadn't really seen what I saw, that it was a person, and I was imagining anything else.

Knowing I couldn't sit there, I headed

towards the lake, still at the puttering five miles per hour. I passed the area where I'd last seen the thing, but didn't see anything. I made it down to the lake and saw a man next to a boat on the shore, which gave me some comfort that maybe I had seen his friend and not a Sasquatch after all.

I went down and turned my car around so I could head straight out. Now parked, I got out with my camera, and I was immediately welcomed by swarms of horseflies, which are prominent in the area during the summer. I took some shots with my camera and made my way to the man, who was still unloading his boat. I asked him why his friend wasn't helping him unload. The man, a native, gave me an odd look and replied that he didn't have any friends there; he was there alone. I told him I'd seen someone just up on the road not too far away. The man gave me a puzzled look and walked away.

I was confused, but I kept taking photos. Now back near my car, I opened my car door when this feeling or sensation of dread overcame me. I didn't get in; I was standing in between the car seat and the open door. I took a picture, this time of the man, but he was now ducking down behind a Polaris Ranger, which I found odd. Then out of nowhere I saw something move in my peripheral view. I turned and got a good look at a massive Sasquatch. This massive creature raced in front of my car, not fifteen feet away, and into the bush.

I jumped back into my car and started it up. My body was shaking uncontrollably. Inside the car, horseflies were everywhere. I rolled the window down, hoping they'd fly out, while at the same time, I put the car into gear and sped off faster than I'd driven in. I wasn't concerned about the potholes; all I could think about was getting out of there and back home.

To my left I heard crashing and something running on two feet. My heart was pounding, my hands were clinging to the steering wheel in a death grip, and I couldn't move fast enough. To this day, that drive to the main highway seemed to take forever. I eventually made it and headed south, as all I wanted to do was be home, in my house. What had taken me six hours to drive to in the morning I did in four hours heading back. The entire drive home I was shaking. I couldn't calm myself down. There was no doubt what I'd seen, none whatsoever, and what made it even more terrifying was how big it was and how close it was to me.

I don't have evidence that the first creature I saw wasn't the same one that ran feet in front of me, but they appeared different. The one on the road I saw walking, head down, towards me looked leaner and its hair was black. Also, the hair on its head and shoulders was longer than what hung lower than that. I call it the '80s rocker look. The one I saw run past the front of the car appeared to be bigger and was grayer in color. I'll never be able to prove they were different or the same; I can only tell you what I saw.

Upon returning home, I told my brother and sister. My brother wanted to go back, but I resisted until he got me to go with a friend weeks later. I am grateful he got me to go back because had he not, I'm not sure I ever would have gone back into the bush. Our first return trip I was able to determine just how close the first sighting was to the second, about three hundred feet, and we marked how tall the first one I saw was by measuring a tree branch close by to where it ran back into the bush. We've since gone back about six or seven more times. We've never seen anything else, and I don't know if I ever will. I know that both my sightings were just flukes. I wasn't out in search of them; I just happened to run up on them by chance. I am grateful also that I have had my run-ins with them, but I can't deny that both times I was scared shitless, with the second encounter leaving me utterly terrified and shaking uncontrollably for hours.

These creatures exist and are bigger than

you can imagine with your mind's eye, so if you have a desire to see one in person, prepare yourself and be careful what you wish for.

I CAN STILL SEE IT
LOOKING AT ME

*S*ome accounts I get come from people who want to share but not on the program for fear that someone might recognize their voice. This is sad yet also validates one of the purposes for my show. I am here to give people a place to come and share without repercussion, but even if you can't come on the show, I'm available to hear your account. Sometimes all people need is someone they can trust to tell their story to. Just recounting their terrifying encounters is the first step towards healing from such an experience. The story below is one of those.

If anyone who's reading this book has a story to tell, yet doesn't feel comfortable coming on my podcast, I'll read it and even share it via my blog *without ever divulging who you are, and ensure your identity is secure.*

***

I grew up on a farm in southern Pennsylvania. My immediate family, including grandparents, aunts and uncles, all lived adjacent to each other on this land. If you totaled all the land together, it came to over one hundred acres, most of it wooded. The wooded parts were thick with old hardwoods like oak, maple, and various pines. Large streams and creeks cut through the land, which eventually spilled into a river close by. The land had abundant wildlife, like whitetail deer, squirrel, fox and the occasional wild turkey.

Growing up, I spent many days hunting, mainly squirrel or deer. In fact, in my high school days, I'd often return home during squirrel season, which stretched from September through December, and get my rifle, either a Winchester Model 94 chambered for .22 caliber or a Ruger 77/22 bolt-action rifle. Both had nice scopes on them and were highly effective for taking the little tree rats. I would go out by myself sometimes, but also hunted with my cousins who lived close by.

One afternoon in October I went out alone. I was sixteen at the time and needed to stretch my legs and think; the woods and hunting was a good place for that. As I hiked along, my mind was somewhere else. Being sixteen, I now had girls on the brain, and my thoughts were plagued by typical teenage drama. When I finally snapped out of my daze, I noticed I was in a part of the woods I'd never been to. I was surrounded by old-growth trees; their trunks were easily four to five feet in diameter. The terrain around me had shifted from fairly flat to rolling hills that dove deep and narrow.

I found myself standing atop these hills, looking down into the bottom of a hollow where a large grove of laurel sat thick and tall. I slowly made my way down and suddenly was overcome with a heavy feeling of dread and the uncomfortable sensation that I was being watched. This feeling was so heavy I froze and began to look around, expecting to see another person but didn't.

This fear kept growing to the point that I felt truly scared, like nothing I'd ever felt before. It was such an odd sensation. My head spun around. I looked left then right, but saw nothing; however, I couldn't get this feeling to stop. Suddenly I saw movement in the laurel followed by the distinct sounds of footfalls and branches snapping. I called out to whoever or whatever was in the laurel that I wasn't alone, hoping that would give whoever it was pause. It worked, the footfalls stopped, but my fear was still amplified. My hands gripped the Ruger 77/22 tightly, and out of an abundance of caution because of the fear that was racing through me, I raised the rifle and leveled it at the laurel.

I again called out. I wanted to make clear to whoever was there that I wasn't alone nor would I be trifled with. This is when things got terrifyingly weird, as I got a response from the laurel in the way of chattering. That's the best way to describe it. Over the years I've wondered if it could be defined differently, but I can't. It legitimately sounded like someone was chattering.

I raised my rifle just above the laurel, and out of fear, I squeezed off a round, hoping I'd strike fear in whatever was there. All I can say now is that it didn't work; in fact, the opposite happened, as all hell broke loose. The chattering became a distinct growl followed by crashing. I could see the top of the bushes moving, and it was clearly coming towards me.

I again called out that I wasn't alone by saying the names of my cousins. It didn't work. It kept crashing through the laurel and coming towards me. I didn't hesitate; I cycled the bolt of my rifle, chambered another .22-caliber round, and fired. This time I didn't shoot over the laurel but into it.

I'm sure the hunters out there reading this

are cursing at me, as I had violated every basic firearm and hunting rule. Yes, I had fired at something I couldn't identify, but all I can say in my defense was I was sixteen at the time, filled with pure terror, and literally felt like this was a life-or-death scenario. If you could have heard this thing, I challenge anyone with a rifle not to fire.

My second shot didn't faze it. Whatever it was kept coming. Not willing to take a stand, I turned and ran up the slope. Now I should mention that it was dusk, the light was going fast, and by how far I'd gone, I wouldn't get back to my house until after dark. When I crested the top of the hill, I looked back and saw something hairy come out of the laurel and look up at me. The distance between me and it was about seventy-five to a hundred yards, if I recall. As I write this, I'm getting a chill up my spine because I can still see it looking at me. Out of pure instinct, I cycled the bolt on the rifle and fired at it without even aiming through my scope, a ten-by-forty

Tasco. I have to assume that I missed because it didn't respond or flinch; all it did was fully emerge and stand. I took a few seconds to look at it before turning on a dime and racing away. What I saw wasn't big, maybe about five to six feet in height, and it was covered in long black hair. Its arms were long and its shoulders were broad. I couldn't make out its face or too much detail, as I was a distance away, like I said, and the light was diminishing.

As I sprinted, I kept tripping and falling. I knew the direction I needed to go but also knew I was a ways out. I had a good ten or fifteen minutes to travel. My heart was pumping, and all I could think was that I needed to get home or I might die out here. I suddenly heard heavy footfalls crashing behind me. This only intensified my desire to get home. I ran through low-hanging branches, cutting my face and hands as I went. I tried to jump over fallen trees only to trip, my rifle taking a beating.

The footfalls soon changed direction and were now parallel to me. It had caught up but didn't run me down; instead it was pacing me to my right. I didn't know what to think; I just knew I needed to get out of the woods and home. I thank God now that I was a runner at the time because I don't know if I could have kept the pace I was going on pure adrenaline otherwise.

Ten minutes must have passed with this thing pacing me before I crested a slight rise and could see the lights of my house just through the trees. If I took the normal path, I'd intersect with this thing. With no other option, I veered left, swept down a hill, rounded it at the base, and burst out of the woods into a large field next to the side of my house. I began to scream for help, but there was no way anyone could hear me. I stopped, cycled the bolt of the rifle one last time, turned and fired again into the woods. All I can say is that little rifle felt like the one thing that could protect me, although I'm sure it wouldn't have done any good against it. I paused and listened after I fired. I heard nothing. The woods were silent and still. My heart was thumping hard and sweat mixed with blood streamed down my face. For some reason though I sensed it was in the woods still and watching me, I could feel it. Not wanting to wait around, I turned and ran into the house.

I broke down the second I closed the door behind me. My mom found me and saw my face was cut up and covered in blood, as were my hands. I was a total mess. Tears streamed down my face and I kept blathering on about seeing a monster. She consoled me and cleaned up my cuts. She said that it was probably just a bear; I told her that it wasn't, although I'd never seen a bear in real life at this time. She then told me a story about a time something came to her house when she was growing up, her childhood home was literally several hundred yards away, and tore down a huge branch and caused a bunch of damage. She was told back then by my grandfather that it was a bear too, although I now have my suspicions.

My older brother overheard what I was saying to my mom. He went to the gun cabinet, grabbed a shotgun, and went out to see if he could find the thing. I encouraged him not to, and my mom forbade it, but he went out anyway. I couldn't just let him go, so I followed after reloading my rifle's magazine.

It was now pitch black out. We crossed the field to the edge of the woods. He hollered out some obscenities and fired the shotgun into the woods. I can only say now that this was his way of 'protecting and standing up' for his little brother.

We didn't hear a twig break, and after a few minutes of standing there, we went back inside. That night I couldn't stop talking about it. My father was out of town and I couldn't wait to tell him. That night I found it hard to sleep even though I was exhausted, not just from the run of my life but from the intense adrenaline dump I'd had.

My dad came home and I told him. He laughed it off and, like my mom, said it was probably a black bear. My sister and oldest brother also thought it was a bear too. I then began to wonder if I had mistaken the identity of this thing, and stopped bringing it up, as some in my family began to ridicule me.

The one person who never doubted me was my grandmother; she'd lived on the farm for fifty-five years and proceeded to tell me stories about odd things she'd seen—shadows in the woods and lights. She questioned whether it really was a bear that had broken off the huge branch near their house years before. It felt good to have someone I trusted believe me. Even though I did have someone like her who didn't think I was crazy, I kept my story to myself unless I was around company I thought I could share with.

I have to admit that my pragmatic self has wondered if I did see a bear and mistook it, but then I'll quickly push that aside, as I can still see that thing exiting the laurel and looking up at me as if it had a human shape. Even though it was at a distance, I don't recall ever seeing a snout. What I saw wasn't huge, wasn't the typical-looking Bigfoot, but as I drift back to that day, my memory wants to say it looked chimp like. It took me years to finally go back into the woods, but I never ventured into them without a firearm. I know some of you are saying that any type of rifle or pistol wouldn't have an effect, and that may be true, but that's also theoretical. I'll just say that I'd rather have something than nothing. Call it peace of mind.

I'll never know for sure, nor will I ever be able to prove what I saw to anyone; I can only share with you that deep in the southern Pennsylvania woods lurks something that if provoked, will chase after you and leave an indelible imprint on your life.

I LOOKED INTO ITS EYES

*H*ave you ever felt like you're being watched? Of course you have; we all have had that feeling before. The thing is that when you do, it's usually because someone is watching you. This brings me to a type of encounter that many share, and those are of the creature approaching homes and peering through windows. This says a lot about their personality and recognizes that they have a curiosity about us that's probably equal to ours about them.

I don't know what I'd do if I looked out and saw a massive face of one of those creatures looking back in at me.

***

This happened back in the 1970s up in

northern Maryland near the Pennsylvania border. My late husband and I lived in a community that backed up against a large swatch of forest. This forest was large and extended for miles in length and width; if I were to guess, I'd say it was about three hundred acres back then. It's now been chopped up and developed.

At this time my husband was a Maryland state trooper and was working the third shift, which put him on the road from late evening until the early morning. I hated when he worked these shifts, but such is the life of a trooper's wife. For a couple of weeks I had smelled a pungent odor out behind our house during the hours my husband was gone. I mentioned it to him, and he said it was more than likely a skunk. He was an avid hunter, so I took him at his word.

Our living room faced the backyard, and in the living room we had a large picture window. Our couch was just below it, and it's where I sat to sew while I watched television.

Almost nightly the odor came around. At first I ignored it; then I began to turn on the lights in the back to see if I could see the skunk and shoo it away, of course praying it didn't spray at the same time. Each time I never saw a thing, although I do recall once hearing something in the woods making some noise through the dry leaves. I thought nothing of this, as we often got critters like deer and fox coming around.

The particular night in question, I was sitting watching a show on PBS. I recall this because each detail of what happened next is seared into my memory. The smell returned, but something was different. I felt as if I was being watched. I've felt that sensation before in my life, but now it was intense. I lifted my head from what I was sewing and looked at the television. The hairs on the back of my head rose, and I just knew there was something just behind me. I instantly became afraid and didn't know what to do. On the end table next to me was our phone, I thought about picking it up and calling my husband via dispatch, but I thought that was premature, as I was only having a feeling. I wanted to look back, but I just feared that there would be something there, so I stayed frozen.

I can't tell you how long this went on, but it seemed like forever. I kept going back and forth, debating myself, until I found the courage to look over my shoulder. When I craned my head back, I immediately recoiled, as I was looking into someone's face, although this wasn't a person, this was something else. I yelped and jumped from the couch, dropping my needle and thread. I rushed away from the couch, almost tripping over the coffee table. Whatever it was in the window, it followed my movements with its eyes then pulled away from the window, disappearing into the darkness. I immediately ran to the back door, turned on the lights, and looked out through the glass in the door to see something large and dark running across the backyard towards the woods. I checked to make sure the door was locked, and went to the phone on the wall in the kitchen and dialed the barracks dispatch. I told them I needed to reach my husband and that I had an intruder at our house. After I got off the phone, I rushed to our bedroom closet and got a shotgun. I can still feel how scared I was. My hands were trembling and I couldn't quite get the face out of my mind.

My husband arrived at the house in about ten minutes. He raced inside the house, his revolver drawn, and went immediately towards the back door. I told him I thought whoever or whatever it was was gone. He unlocked and threw open the door and exited, his revolver in one hand and a big Maglite in his other. He walked around the yard and to the edge of the woods. The pungent odor was still lingering though it was faint. He went to the spot at the window and made out some large impressions in the mulch. He walked the perimeter of the house numerous times before coming back in.

I described what I saw and he dismissed the idea. How I described it then is such: the head was large, very large, and the face was wide, with wide-set eyes, about six inches or so separating them. The nose was flat, sort of like an ape's, and the face had hair on it, though it wasn't completely covered. Its eyes were round and black; that's what scared me the most was its eyes and how they tracked me when I jumped up. The thing didn't appear scared, but did snap back after a bit and took off running.

For many years I kept trying to convince myself that what I saw was a man wearing a mask, but I can't deny it anymore. What came to my window was a Sasquatch. I don't know why, but for some reason it was drawn to our house. I do wonder if it kept coming because I was alone. My husband was able to change shifts because of what happened, and whatever it was never returned.

Anytime I sit down now, I make sure my

back is never to a window, or if it is, I make sure the blinds or drapes are drawn. I never want to ever look back and see a face staring back at me again.

MISTAKEN IDENTITY

*O*ne profession that over the years I've heard from are police officers. The internet, in fact, has many dash cam videos of 'things' crossing the road. In my opinion, police officers offer credibility to encounters because they are coming forward at the risk of their professional reputation. I know many people in general are worried about their reputations, hence why they don't publically discuss encounters, but a police officer does run the risk of losing their job. The next story details an officer who was called out to a woman's house. She would not share the account, but what the officer ran into while there is enough to make this story terrifying.

***

When the following occurred, I was a new

deputy for the sheriff's department, recently hired and straight out of the police academy. The county I worked in back then was a rural county, mostly farmland around, with occasional livestock. I don't want to give away exactly where it was, but it was located in a state along the eastern seaboard. Being that I was new, I was given the third shift to patrol. That meant I worked from the late evening until the early morning. My area to patrol was pretty large, spanning most of the southern part of the county, which meant I had an area to respond to that was about one hundred square miles. I know that seems like a lot, but the county was rural with a relatively small population.

The particular night in question happened in springtime. It was a cool mid early morning and a fog had set in. I got a call from dispatch about a woman who said someone was at her residence. There wasn't much beyond that. The call in question was about a fifteen-minute drive. Not hesitating, I sped over there.

When I arrived, I found the house sat down a long gravel drive that stretched about two-tenths of a mile long. At the end of the drive was an older two-story house. Through the thick fog I could see fields on either side but not much else past that. I was alert and keeping an eye out for anyone who might be around, but saw no one, nor did I spot any suspicious vehicles. I had a light on the outside of my cruiser, and I turned it on and scanned the area, but the fog was making it difficult to see much. I finally made my way to the house and parked. With my flashlight in hand, I exited my cruiser and headed to the closest door, which was a side door.

Before I could knock, I heard the deadbolt turn and the door flew open. Standing before me was an older woman about sixty to seventy years old. She was draped in a tattered robe, and on her feet were slippers. Her gray hair was pulled back tight, and by the look on her face she appeared scared.

I opened my mouth to ask about the call

and she interrupted me. She told me that something was just at the house and banging on her window. She said it just left the second I pulled up. Upon hearing this, I headed to the spot but didn't find anything. I flashed my light all around, but the fog made it impossible. I did a good search of the property but found nothing, nor any clues. I returned to the side door to find her standing where I'd left her. I asked her to give me a detailed account. This is what she told me.

"I was preparing to go to bed when I heard a loud slap on the side of my house. At first I didn't think much of it. A second and louder slap then followed. I got scared and went to my bedroom to get my shotgun. From there I made sure all the doors were locked. As I headed to the kitchen, I saw something move in the window over the sink. I rushed to the window to look out but saw nothing but darkness. A loud slap came from my spare bedroom. I hurried through the house, my shotgun in my hand. When I turned on the lights in the room, I saw movement in the south-facing window,

but couldn't make out what it was. That was when I got scared and called 911. These slaps have been occurring until you arrived."

I asked her if she knew who it might be. Was it a neighbor? Was someone she knew not happy with her or could be pranking her? She replied no to both questions. I could see that she was terrified. I took a full report and assured her that whoever it was, they were now gone. The hour was getting early, as I could see it was getting light outside. I said my goodbyes and headed to my cruiser.

Outside, the fog was lifting. Just as I was about to get in, her door opened, and she shouted, "It's in the field!" She pointed to my right. I looked and saw something tall, dark and standing on two feet about a hundred yards away. I rushed to a fence and shouted towards the figure. It turned and sprinted off to a finger of woods close by. I raced back to my cruiser, started it and sped off. I figured that I could catch whoever it was if I drove. The finger of woods connected with the county road. I sped down the driveway, turned left and headed to about the area it would be, when something massive ran out in front of me. I slammed on my brakes and looked at what I can say was a big hairy man-type creature. It was tall, with long arms, and its face looked like that of a man's but covered in hair with darkish skin.

In what must have been two steps it cleared the county road and went into the woods on my right. I wasn't sure what I'd just seen, but hopped out of my car. I had my lights on and, with my flashlight in hand, scanned the woods, but didn't see anything. I was tempted to go in pursuit on foot, but something in my guts told me not to, that what I'd be going after wasn't a person but something else.

I got back in the comfort and security of my cruiser and picked up the radio. I can't say how long I held it in my hand, but I hesitated to call in what I'd just seen. Who would believe me? Before this, I had heard of Bigfoot, but thought it wasn't anywhere close to being in the eastern states. I thought it lived in northern California or Washington State. I finally called in that I'd left the woman's house and that I'd seen a man in the field, but I deliberately left out that I'd seen it run in front of me and that I thought it wasn't a man at all.

I went back to the office, finalized the report, and again conveniently left that bit of information out. I know I was being self-serving, but who would have believed me, and I needed this job. I truly feared that if I told the sheriff I'd seen Bigfoot, that he would have sent me to get a psych evaluation, something I couldn't afford to get. I had always wanted to be in law enforcement, and if I told them what I'd seen, I could probably kiss my job goodbye.

I never saw it again, nor did the woman ever call in again. I don't know where it went or if it was just passing through. Since I had heard from a couple of guys who worked at the Department of Natural Resources that they'd seen some 'odd' things like what I'd seen, and I did share my encounter with others I trusted, but I have never openly told my story to anyone, and that's been close to thirty years now.

All I can say is that I can still see the raw fear in the woman's eyes when she opened the door, and I can still see that massive thing sprinting across the road in my headlights as clear as the second I'd seen it. What she thought was a person wasn't that at all, it was a Bigfoot, and I still today wonder why it was taunting her. I'll never know, but I do cringe when I think back to when I was walking around in the fog outside her house that that thing was there probably feet away staring at me. Gives me goose bumps just to think about that.

BEYOND THE FRAY: BIGFOOT

MY WASHINGTON STATE
EXPERIENCE

*A*fter so many have shared their encounters
*with me over the years, some of which
you've just read, I believe I have to pony
up an experience that I and others had while out
searching for Bigfoot. While this experience doesn't
include an actual encounter with the creature, it
will detail a sighting of orbs or balls of light, a
phenomenon that many associate with Sasquatch.*

*The phenomenon of seeing bright orbs or balls
of light either before, during or after sightings of
the creature have many now assuming they're
associated with each other. It also has some
theorizing that Sasquatch could be an inter-
dimensional being or be connected to UFOs. Now
I'm not stating those theories are true, nor am I
debunking them. I only know what I saw and can
say that it happened and did so in a place that is
widely known for Sasquatch sightings and activity.*

***

The Brown property in Washington State is famous for Sasquatch activity. Over the years, many investigators have gone to Sara and Jon Brown's property; one of those being the Olympic Project, and it was there they captured the famous Linebacker on the Ridge thermal video.

So when I had the opportunity to go, I didn't hesitate. It was October of 2014 and I, along with Wes Germer and Kirk Brandenburg, headed there with high expectations.

We arrived and immediately got to work. The Browns gave us a tour of the property, showing us various locations where they've had sightings and activity. Night quickly came and we found ourselves back at the house, making plans and strategizing. We plotted exactly where we'd conduct our research but also wanted to finalize specifically what tactics we'd use to elicit activity and draw the creature in.

When the clock struck nine, we had our plan and destination. We grabbed our gear and headed out; however, Sara stopped us on her way to put her kids to bed and pointedly asked us *not* to go to a set of abandoned buildings adjacent to their property. We acknowledged her request and marched out into the dark of night, excited for what lay ahead.

With our senses heightened, we navigated the property, eventually finding our way into a valley and to a stream that coursed through the bottom of it. Knowing that Sasquatch can often be found near water, we followed the stream, which coincidently took us to…the abandoned buildings Sara warned us not to go to.

Obviously curious, we took out our flashlights and examined the dilapidated relics. The roof was intact on the one closest to us, but in some places, the exterior walls were nothing more than two-by-four framing and no siding.

It had been raining lightly on and off all night, but as if timed perfectly, the sky opened up and began to dump on us. Even though we had come prepared, we didn't want to get drenched by the heavy cold rain, so we took shelter in the abandoned building. We were inside for no more than a few minutes when Kirk said, "Who is that coming towards us?"

We all went to the closest opening in a wall and peered out to see a light moving very fast and smooth through the forest on the ravine across from us. As I stared, I first thought it must be some crazy person racing through the woods in the cold heavy rain. To me the light appeared white, while the others seemed to register it as blue or even slightly orange.

Kirk pulled out his thermal monocular scope and put it to his eye. He voiced that he saw no heat signature, nor could he register anything remotely that looked like a person running.

Just as quickly as it had appeared, it vanished by diving into the ground. With urgency, Kirk climbed through the space in the wall while the rest of us went quickly out the door we came in and headed towards where Kirk was. Before we could meet up with Kirk, we heard three loud slaps on the second building. It sounded as if someone with an open hand had struck it hard. We immediately went to investigate but found nothing.

We were left confused as to how something could hit the building then flee so quickly. Kirk was equally perplexed, as he couldn't explain why his thermal never saw any heat signature. The rain suddenly abated, and with all in agreement, we headed back to the Browns' house, with no physical or eyewitness evidence but nevertheless excited about what had happened on our first night there.

***

It was the final evening at the Browns'. We were set up in their backyard, which overlooked a wide valley. It was cold, drizzling, and getting close to midnight. Our plan was not to go looking for them; instead we were going to lure them in to us. Using a recorded cry of a baby (see Chapter Three), we set Wes' phone twenty yards from us in the woods and hit play. Over and over the looped recording went of the baby crying for an hour. Unable to take any more of the maddening sound, Sara said her goodbyes and went back to the house. Not a few minutes after was when things got interesting.

Off in the woods, a short distance away, a soft whoop came.

We were instantly excited. Another whoop followed close behind that. Soon the whoops became perfectly rhythmic in sets of three and had a singsong quality to them. They also sounded feminine to us.

Forty-five minutes went by with the whoops continuing in the same three-set pattern. Whatever it was, it wasn't far from us or the phone. Then without notice, Wes' phone died, and instantly, the whoops stopped too. We grabbed another phone and started the cries, but the whoops didn't continue. Whatever had been interested had gone away or was now just silent and watching us. We continued on but never heard anything the rest of the night. It is disappointing and disheartening to say that we did record that night, but the sound of the drizzling rain drowned out any other sounds.

We left the next day without concrete evidence of a sighting but didn't view our time spent as a failure.

In closing, I am not claiming what was experienced during these events was definitely a Sasquatch, as I did not, nor did anyone, get a visual of what was making these whoops or slaps. They were, however, very interesting and occurred in a hot spot of verified Sasquatch activity so hence are worthy of being noted.

IN CONCLUSION

If you've made it this far, let me first say thank you. The encounters you've just read are a tiny fraction of the many cases and eyewitness accounts that exist. I am honored that these folks trusted in me to come on my show then allowed me to share them in this book. The amazing thing to ponder is the thousands of other cases or encounters that are out there, and the other thousands that have never been told, as those people are fearful to say a word.

Every time I interview someone, I always imagine I'm in their shoes. I do this because I want to get a sense of what I'd do in the situation. Would I handle things differently? Would I be grateful for the encounter, or would I be forever haunted by it? So often, we as people hear stories and instantly make assumptions; some good and some bad. We pass judgment on people all based upon narrow belief systems; just because we've never had the experience doesn't mean it never occurred. I will always listen with an open ear and an empathetic heart.

The mystery of Bigfoot has captivated many people, including myself, and has spawned everything in popular culture from television shows to toys. Many people are truly fascinated, and while they all may not be believers, deep down they are curious. I don't know if we'll ever have enough scientific evidence to prove without a doubt that Sasquatch exists to the masses and the naysayers. I actually believe that some people are so closed off to the possibility that we could film a Sasquatch and a hunter playing patty cake from six feet away in 4K UHD for an hour straight, and it still wouldn't satisfy some.

What I can say for myself is I'm a hopeful believer. There is so much more than just a good possibility this creature is out there, and for some reason—maybe because it's the ultimate hide-and-seek champion or because there's something even more mystical happening—it keeps eluding us. Theories and conjecture abound. The more time that goes on, and the more they continue to elude us…the more questions pile on. Are they this smart…this good? Are we this inferior in the woods? Are our tactics too arcane? At what age do they get sent to 'Avoid Humans For Life Training Camp'? Whatever the answer, I do hope we get it one day.

It has been my honor to present this collection of encounters, and I hope you've been at the minimum entertained and hopefully enlightened. If any of you have had your own encounter and want to share it with me, please don't hesitate to send me an e-mail: shannon@intothefrayradio.com.

ABOUT THE AUTHORS

Shannon LeGro has been examining the paranormal since she was a teen after having her own personal experience She strives to bring a fresh perspective and an open mind to the most intriguing mysteries in our universe. She is the host & producer of the popular podcast, iNTO THE FRAY and can also be heard as a guest host on the show Midnight In Desert. You can also see her in the Small Town Monsters production, On the Trail of Bigfoot and in the upcoming documentary, On the Trail of UFOs.

Visit Shannon online at www.intothefrayradio.com

G. Michael Hopf is the USA Today bestselling author of almost forty novels including his international bestselling post-apocalyptic series, THE NEW WORLD. He has made a prominent name for himself in both the post-apocalyptic and western genres. He is co-founder of Beyond The Fray Publishing & Doomsday Press. He is a combat veteran of the United States Marine Corps and whiskey aficionado.

Visit G. Michael Hopf at www.gmichaelhopf.com

BEYOND THE FRAY: BIGFOOT

Made in the USA
Columbia, SC
03 June 2022

61306232R00133